'I thought I ha[ ] wanted.'

'You have somethi[ ]

Putting her glasses ᵇᵃᶜᵏ ᵒⁿ, wasn't offering myself.'

He raised a dark brow. 'Suppose you tell me what you *were* offering and what you expected in return.'

'I wanted a husband... *in name only*,' she added swiftly, 'for a year.'

Dear Reader

As Easter approaches, Mills & Boon are delighted to present you with an exciting selection of sixteen new titles. Why not take a trip to our Euromance locations— Switzerland or western Crete, where romance is celebrated in great style! Or maybe you'd care to dip into the story of a family feud or a rekindled love affair? Whatever tickles your fancy, you can always count on love being in the air with Mills & Boon!

The Editor

Lee Wilkinson lives with her husband in a three-hundred-year-old stone cottage in a Derbyshire village, which most winters gets cut off by snow. They both enjoy travelling and recently, joining forces with their daughter and son-in-law, spent a year going round the world 'on a shoe-string' while their son looked after Kelly, their much loved German shepherd. Her hobbies are reading and gardening and holding impromptu barbecues for her long-suffering family and friends.

Recent titles by the same author:

LOST LADY

ADAM'S ANGEL

BY
LEE WILKINSON

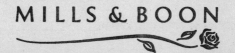

MILLS & BOON

MILLS & BOON LIMITED
ETON HOUSE, 18-24 PARADISE ROAD
RICHMOND, SURREY TW9 1SR

*First published in Great Britain 1994
by Mills & Boon Limited*

© Lee Wilkinson 1994

*Australian copyright 1994
Philippine copyright 1994
This edition 1994*

ISBN 0 263 78455 X

*Set in Times Roman 10 on 11¼ pt.
01-9404-52731 C*

Made and printed in Great Britain

CHAPTER ONE

HALLFIELD'S church clock was chiming midnight as Angie drove homewards through the small village, with its half-timbered pub and straggle of stone cottages.

It was a pitch-black night, a thick blanket of cloud blotting out both moon and stars as she left the hamlet behind her and followed the narrow, winding Derbyshire lane with care.

Her ancient Ford's headlights made a ghostly tunnel, picking out the white flowering may shrouding the hawthorn trees that flanked the dry stone walls. To someone strange it might have seemed lonely and spooky, but Angie was on home ground.

A break in the wall on the left signalled the track leading to the diverse pair of neighbouring cottages that stood merely a hundred yards apart, and a bare half-mile from Wingwood Hall, as the crow flew.

In the past, old Mr Dawson's square two up, two down cottage had served as a beacon, but for the last three months, since he'd retired from his job as the Hall's caretaker and gone to join his son in Canada, it had stood dark and empty.

Until tonight.

A flash of light in the front room made Angie stand on the brake. She had stopped the engine and opened the car door before prudence suggested a second thought or two might not come amiss.

Admittedly she was 'keeping an eye' on Fife Cottage, and had a set of keys, but that didn't necessarily mean it was wise to go charging in. If it turned out to be a burglar—and who else was likely to be flashing a torch in an empty house at twelve o'clock at night?—the nearest stalwart male lived in Hallfield.

Of course she could fetch Tosca.

But though Tosca *looked* fierce, the English bull-terrier was an uncertain ally, being both idle and soft as grease.

That seemed to leave only one course of action. She must drive back to the phone box at the crossroads and dial 999.

She was about to switch on the ignition when once again prudence stuck in an oar. Suppose the flash she'd seen had been nothing more sinister than her own headlights briefly reflected in the dark panes? She *had* turned the wheel sharply to avoid a deep rut that grooved the track. If she dragged the police out here on a false alarm...

The least she could do was see if there were any signs of a forced entry. Settling her spectacles more firmly on her nose, Angie felt in her bag for the small torch she carried and, switching off the car's lights, climbed out.

Unable to drive comfortably in the high heels she'd worn that evening, she'd kicked them off and was in stockinged feet.

Her eyes adjusted to the blackness, and, moving carefully on the rough ground, she passed the large, double-doored wooden shed which had always done duty as Mr Dawson's garage. Feeling for the catch of the garden gate, she made her way silently up the paved path.

Switching on the torch, she examined the green door. Apart from a light veneer of accumulated dirt, its paint was unblemished and free from jemmy marks.

Sneaking past the living-room window—just in case— she made her way round the side of the cottage. Neither the kitchen casements nor the back door showed any signs of an illicit entry, and a check proved the latter was still securely locked.

She turned, her sigh of relief changing to a strangled squawk of fear as she blundered straight into the arms of the waiting figure, dropping the torch and dislodging her glasses.

The man was big and muscular and she was no match for his strength, but, instead of keeping cool and employing the self-defence she'd been taught, abysmal terror made her fight like a tigress.

'Hold still, damn you,' he snarled. 'I don't want to have to hurt you.'

A blow from her flailing fist finding its mark on a hard cheekbone apparently made him change his mind. Seizing her arm, he forced it up her back until sheer pain kept her motionless. 'That's better,' he muttered, and, hustling her round to the front of the house, opened the door and pushed her inside.

As she stumbled forward a few paces she heard the door close and turned to look straight into the beam of a powerful torch.

'Well, I'm damned!' the man exclaimed. 'I'm all for equality of the sexes, but a female burglar!'

'D-don't be ridiculous,' Angie stuttered. 'I'm nothing of the kind.'

'So what were you doing examining the doors and windows at this time of night?'

'If you'll stop trying to blind me, I'll tell you...'

The beam was lowered slightly.

'I was looking for signs of a forced entry. I saw a flash as I was driving past and thought *you* were a burglar.'

He grunted non-committally, then asked drily, 'And do you still think so?'

'You're not acting like a burglar,' she admitted. 'Though I can't imagine why else you were creeping about with a torch.'

Sounding irritated, he said, 'I was trying to find the fuse-boxes.'

'They're in a cupboard to your left that forms part of the bookcase.'

The beam was swung in that direction and, once located, the main switch thrown. In a moment light flooded the room, chilly and neglected with its dusty, old-fashioned furniture and empty fireplace.

After blinking in the renewed brightness, Angie stared at her captor with huge golden-brown eyes. He was at least six feet tall and broad-shouldered, with hair the colour of peat, and a lean, hard-bitten face.

Even without her glasses, the lack of which made people and objects alike blur into soft focus, he looked every bit as tough and formidable as her encounter in the dark had suggested.

She repressed a shiver.

Then, wanting to keep the initiative, she took a deep breath and, drawing herself up to her full five feet three, demanded, 'Would you mind telling me who you are and what you're doing here in such suspicious circumstances?'

Her dignified stand was spoilt by her already ruined chignon giving up its precarious hold and drooping drunkenly over one ear, before uncoiling into a silken ash-blonde fall.

His rapier-like glance travelled from her dishevelled head down her slim, apparently boyish figure in its olive-green skirt and jacket, to her stockinged feet. Coolly amused, he countered, 'I might ask you the same.'

After a brief hesitation, she told him, 'My name's Angie Doland; I live in the next cottage. I agreed to keep an eye on this place until the Hall's new caretaker arrives. He should have been here last week, but...' She broke off abruptly. 'Are *you* by any chance...?'

'Yes, in a manner of speaking. I'm Adam Langford.'

The name itself meant nothing. A shade irascibly, now the danger appeared to be over, she asked, 'What on earth made you come so late?'

'My intention was to arrive earlier,' he said with studied patience. 'But I had trouble with my hired car and had to have a new fuel pump fitted before I could travel the last fifty miles.'

'I didn't see a car.' Suspicion returned to paw the ground.

His firm lips twisted. 'And of course you stopped to look in the shed?'

'No,' she admitted, and stared down at her feet, suddenly feeling foolish in the face of his quietly biting sarcasm.

The feeling was intensified when, his gaze having followed hers, his amusement even more apparent, he said, 'Forgive my curiosity, Miss Doland, but do you always take off your shoes to drive?'

'Only when I'm wearing high heels.' Without intending to, she found herself explaining, 'I'd been out to dinner with my fiancé, and——'

Adam Langford frowned. 'And he let you come home on your own to such a lonely spot at this time of night?'

'It's not really lonely,' she protested.

He raised a dark, winged brow in silent comment, making her admit, 'Perhaps it is in a way, now Ben and Mr Dawson are both gone...'

'Who's Ben?'

'My stepfather. He died five months ago.'

The shock of Ben's death was still with her. There wasn't a day that went past without her thinking of him, grieving for him.

He'd been a gentle, contented man who had enjoyed life in his own quiet way, and faced the end with humour and courage.

His one concern had been that Angie's home should be secure, that she should keep the cottage which had been in his family for generations.

Swallowing, she went on with greater firmness, 'I've lived at Clouds since I was a small child. It's never *seemed* lonely. And Simon will be moving in with me as soon as we're married. In any case, I can take care of myself.'

'I beg leave to doubt that. Though you certainly put up a good fight.'

'Oh...' Even without her glasses, she could see that his left eye was beginning to darken and puff up. 'I'm sorry. But you shouldn't have sneaked up on me like that.' With some idea of putting things into perspective, she added, 'If I'd kept my head and used the self-defence I've learnt... Well, it could have been worse.'

'I see.' His deep voice was wry. 'I must bear that in mind for the future... Was it your fiancé who taught you?'

'Oh, no!' Despite herself, she sounded shocked. 'It was Ben who insisted I take the course. Simon doesn't approve.'

And she'd always sought his approval. Happy, even *grateful* that he was helping her carry out Ben's dying wish, she'd tried hard to turn herself into the kind of woman he wanted.

Unexpectedly, Adam Langford chuckled. 'Running scared, is he?'

'Of course not,' she denied quickly. 'But what I do reflects on him, and he has a position to think about.' She flushed a little, aware as she repeated them that Simon's words sounded pompous.

But he had struggled long and hard to secure a foothold in the town's top society.

Weakly she admitted, 'He doesn't consider it...ladylike...for want of a better word.'

'Is being "ladylike" more important than your personal safety?' When she ignored the sardonic question, Adam asked, 'And what does this paragon do? Do you work for him?'

Lifting her chin, she answered, 'No, I work in a library. Or at least I used to... Simon owns an extremely successful estate agency.'

'My, my...' Adam murmured, sounding impressed.

Disregarding the spurious admiration, she got down to practicalities. 'Have you any steak?'

'Thinking of staying for supper?'

'I mean for your eye.'

'I haven't any steak, and, believe me, if I had I'd eat it.'

'Didn't you bring any supplies with you?'

'No,' he answered shortly. 'I planned to shop in the village.'

'Bad planning, I'm afraid,' she murmured sweetly, getting her own back for his digs at Simon. 'Even if you'd arrived when the shop was open, to buy so much as a loaf you have to order it a day in advance.'

'Thank you,' he said, smoothly sarcastic. 'I'll make a note of that.' Then, with some asperity, 'There's really no need to keep staring at me with such wide-eyed intensity. I'm not plotting a surprise attack.'

'It's not that... When you grabbed me earlier I lost my glasses.'

'Well, let's hope they're not broken.' He picked up the heavy, rubber-covered torch he'd put down on the bookcase, and opened the door. 'I'll retrieve them for you.'

'Wouldn't it be quicker to go the back way?'

He gave her a look that held exasperation. 'It would, except that I only have the front key.'

'I've got a set,' she announced. 'But they're at home.'

His silence more eloquent than words, he departed.

No wonder she hadn't heard him creeping up on her, Angie thought, as she stood in the open doorway and watched him disappear round the side of the cottage; he moved so lithely and silently.

He was back in a moment or two, carrying her dark-framed spectacles and her torch, both of which had miraculously survived the fall and the ensuing scuffle.

Having thanked him, Angie donned the large, owlish glasses with a feeling of relief, which turned to consternation as she saw the full extent of the damage to his eye.

'Yes,' he said grimly. 'For someone so small, you really pack a punch.'

She shook her head deprecatingly. 'It was just a lucky blow.'

Judging by his baleful expression, he wasn't exactly thrilled with what had been meant as an apology.

'Well, goodnight,' she murmured hastily. 'I'll let you have your keys in the morning.'

When she'd driven the short distance to Clouds and turned into the drive, she stopped a little way from the 'garage' and switched off her lights, not wanting to disturb the swallows who nested there.

Not that they were easily disturbed. After countless seasons of returning faithfully to the same site, they regarded as their own the ivy-covered open-fronted barn-type building, with its crumbling brickwork and sagging roof.

The cottage, on the other hand, was pristine and lovely, a four-hundred-year-old black and white timber-framed gem of a place.

It had been built copying a style known as Wealden, in which parts of the upper storey and sides projected as jetties.

The internal plan, a central hall open to the roof with a parlour on one side, a large buttery on the other, and an oak staircase leading to four bedrooms and then attics, had remained more or less unchanged, except that one of the bedrooms had been turned into a bathroom, the parlour had become a through living-room, and the buttery a morning-room with a modern kitchen and a second bathroom at the rear.

As always, the bull-terrier, her big black nose clapped to the crack at the bottom of the door, was waiting, snuffling furiously as Angie let herself into the hall.

Tosca's welcome was akin to grievous bodily harm, and Angie had—of necessity—become adept at fending her off until the first paroxysms of delight had spent themselves.

Having given the fawn and white bitch a generous amount of fuss, Angie was heading for the kitchen to make their nightly cocoa, when her conscience began to nag.

Her new neighbour wouldn't be able to have a bedtime drink, nor an early morning cup of tea. And, judging by his remark about the steak, he hadn't stopped for an evening meal, so he was no doubt starving. On top of which his eye probably hurt like hell.

Before her conscience got its second wind, she was reaching for a cardboard box which had contained her groceries. When she'd put in everything she thought he'd need, as a gesture of contrition she added the piece of sirloin she'd bought for tomorrow evening's meal.

Removing the keys to Fife Cottage from the hook they adorned, she took the torch and, balancing the box on her hip, prepared to let herself out.

Disturbed by this unexpected departure, Tosca began to bark and prance.

'All right, you can come,' Angie agreed. 'You'll need a run before bedtime. But behave yourself,' she added severely, 'and no sneaking off.' The bull-terrier had, from a pup, shown a roving disposition completely at odds with her general dislike of exercise.

The lights were still on at Fife Cottage when Angie knocked. Receiving no answer, she did a juggling act with the box and the torch and let herself in, leaving the keys in the lock and the door ajar.

There wasn't a sound.

Realising that Adam Langford was probably making up his bed, she crossed the living-room to open the stairs' door and call, 'Cooee.'

He was five steps from the bottom, his thick dark hair still wet from the shower, totally naked except for the striped towel slung around his neck.

Clutching the box to her chest, Angie goggled at him. He looked bronzed and fit and so superbly male that her breath was strangled in her throat and her heart began to beat a rapid tattoo against her ribs.

Continuing his descent unhurriedly, he reached out and lifted the glasses from her nose.

'It isn't that I'm particularly shy,' he explained drily. 'But your fiancé might not approve of too close a study of another man's anatomy.'

'I—I wasn't...' She found herself stammering helplessly.

'Of course you were,' he said pleasantly.

Blushing scarlet to the roots of her hair, she thrust the box at him and fled, fumbling for the torch button, stumbling in her haste and confusion.

Only when she reached her own front door did she realise that Tosca wasn't with her.

After calling and whistling repeatedly, to no avail, Angie gave up. Shivering a little in the chill night air, muttering imprecations, she locked and bolted the door.

It obviously wasn't her night. During dinner she and Simon had quarrelled yet again. These days they seemed to be at odds more often than not.

Though normally very good-tempered, and *wanting* to please him, she was beginning to resent the way he tried to push her around.

Having no one to share her cocoa, she decided not to bother, but to get straight off to bed. As she cleaned her pearly, not quite even teeth, she stared at her blurred image in the mirror and fancied that her cheeks were still pink from her brush with Apollo next door.

Drat the man! So self-possessed, so coolly amused. She hoped his eye did hurt. It would have given her great satisfaction to black the other one.

Though Fife Cottage had had one of its two bedrooms turned into a large bathroom, the only way to heat the water was a boiler installed behind the open grate, and to her knowledge there had been no fires lit for months. Fancy taking a cold shower at this time of night in an unheated house! Serve the fool right if he got pneumonia...

Still seething uselessly, she took herself off to the narrow bed in the spacious white room she'd slept in since she was three years old.

But the age of childish innocence was past. The images of a tanned and muscular, magnificently virile male body kept her awake and restless, making her heart beat faster and her stomach clench, and causing her to blush hotly at her own erotic thoughts.

Simon had never had such a devastating effect on her. But then she'd never seen Simon without his clothes. She tried to imagine him stripped off.

Her mental picture was traitorously smooth and pale and effete, compared to her new neighbour's marvellous physique.

Next morning Angie was surfacing gradually when the sound of a vehicle coming along the track and idling outside snapped her into complete wakefulness. Wanting to know the time, she felt for her glasses. Their absence trawled up things she would sooner have forgotten.

Mentally sending Adam Langford to purgatory, she pulled on her thin pink cotton dressing-gown and went to the window to peer through one of the diamond-leaded panes.

A small, somewhat battered truck with the name of a building firm stencilled on the side was turning to pull into her drive.

Barefoot, she trotted down the stairs and opened the front door to a lovely June morning. The truck was parked just behind her car and a middle-aged man and a burly youth were unloading heavy hammers and pickaxes into a wheelbarrow.

'Excuse me,' she called. 'I'm afraid you've got the wrong house.'

The older of the two, a man with thinning grey hair and a bad-tempered expression, walked over, pulling a flimsy sheet of yellow paper from his pocket. 'This is Clouds, isn't it? Says so on the gate.'

'Yes, this is Clouds, but——'

Thrusting the paper at her, he stabbed at it with an irritable forefinger. 'There's the address on the work sheet.'

Angie squinted at it. 'I can't see very well without my glasses.'

Impatiently, he read it out.

'It's the right address,' she admitted, 'but——'

'Then can you get someone to move the car? It's in the way and we want to get on. Time's money.'

Annoyed by the surliness of his manner, she said clearly, 'It will save you time if you'll just listen a moment, Mr...?' She paused.

'Hoskins,' he supplied.

'Well it's like this, Mr Hoskins, you do have my address on your sheet, but there's been some mistake, because I haven't asked for any work to be done.'

'*You* might not have done, but somebody did.' He consulted his sheet. 'A Mr Perry. Ordered the old building to be demolished and a double garage built. Wants the job done immediately. He said money was no object, so we agreed to make a start even though it's a weekend. Now if you'll get that car moved——'

'I certainly will not...' Angie halted the flow of furious words with an effort. It was no use venting her anger on the builder. Even if he was singularly lacking in charm, he'd come here on what he thought was a bona fide commission.

Slowly and distinctly she said, 'I won't be moving the car, because I don't want the building demolished. Or certainly not until late autumn.'

'Now see here...' From being merely surly, Mr Hoskins had become positively truculent. 'I want to speak to Mr Perry.'

'So do I,' Angie remarked in a heartfelt voice. If Simon thought he could ride roughshod over her like this...! 'But he isn't here at the moment.'

'Are you Mrs Perry?'

'No, I'm Miss Doland.'

'What's up?' The youth had walked over and was now addressing his boss. 'Don't she want the job done?'

Relieved that it finally appeared to be sinking in, Angie answered firmly, 'No, I don't want the job done. I'm sorry you've been inconvenienced, but it isn't my fault. I suggest you see Mr Perry without delay.'

Looking fit to burst, Mr Hoskins said, 'You told me he wasn't home.'

'I said he wasn't *here*. He did give you an address?'

'This one, and as he owns the place——'

'Who told you that?' she interrupted sharply.

'He did.'

'Then I'm afraid he misinformed you. I'll give you *his* address.' Having done so, she went on, '*I* own this place.' Watching Hoskins's jaw drop, she added for good measure, 'And I give the orders around here, not Mr Perry.'

The sound of applause diverted her attention. She looked up to see Adam Langford, casually dressed in frayed jeans and a white short-sleeved shirt, leaning negligently against the trunk of the old walnut tree.

Lazily he said, 'Well spoken ... But of course I knew you were a woman of spirit.'

Ignoring the newcomer, Mr Hoskins thrust the work-sheet into his pocket and made his way back to the truck.

As soon as the youth had reloaded the various tools and the wheelbarrow and jumped into the cab, the builder reversed out and drove away, with a savage grinding of gears that made Angie wince.

Strolling over, Adam enquired, 'I take it the said Mr Perry is your fiancé.'

'Yes,' she admitted.

'Better watch out,' Adam warned. 'If he's trying to take over *before* you're married, God knows what he'll be like *after*.'

Stung, because a similar thought had occurred to her, Angie said sharply, 'Should I need your advice, Mr Langford, I'll ask for it.'

He grinned, a white, flashing grin that transformed his face and knocked her sideways. 'And hell would freeze over first.'

'Got it in one,' she muttered beneath her breath.

Transferring his attention to the outhouse, he asked curiously, 'Surely a well-built garage would be preferable to that eyesore ... ?'

For years Ben had said much the same, but consideration for his beautiful summer visitors had always prevailed.

'Why didn't you let them knock it down?'

'Because of the swallows,' she answered, as if that explained everything.

Apparently it did. 'Ah! So that's why you said late autumn.'

'That's why.'

'Didn't you discuss it with the boyfriend?'

'*Ad nauseam*. But he said I was just being foolish. You see, he'll want somewhere to garage his Mercedes when we're married in a little over a month's time.'

Adam's mouth quirked. 'So that's why he wants the work done straight away.'

'How long were you listening?' she demanded.

Unrepentantly he answered, 'From the word go. I didn't care much for our friend's attitude. I would have butted in, but I considered you were more than capable of putting up a good fight.' He gave her a glinting look.

With saccharine sweetness she asked. 'How *is* your eye this morning?'

Reaching into his shirt pocket, he produced her glasses. 'See for yourself.'

Recalling vividly the moment he'd lifted them from her nose, Angie felt her face grow hot as she replaced them.

Well aware of what was going through her mind, he watched her blush deepen with a mocking smile that only served to add to her confusion.

A good head taller, he seemed to tower over her, and he was so close that she fancied she could feel his body heat. But, determined he shouldn't have the satisfaction of routing her completely, she looked up at him with what nonchalance she could muster.

The skin above his left cheekbone, she was pleased to note, was an unbecoming shade of puce, though the swelling had died down. She also noted, with a queer flutter in the region of her heart, that his heavy-lidded eyes were a beautiful dark greeny-blue, thickly lashed, and slanting upwards slightly at the outer corners.

Dragging her gaze away with an effort, she remarked a shade wildly, 'Simon says I should wear contact lenses . . .'

'I see now where that silly game got its name.' Adam's voice was caustic in the extreme.

Cursing herself, Angie backed into the house, and, preparing to close the door, said stiffly, 'Thank you for returning my glasses.'

'Think nothing of it.' His ironic glance took in her pale tumble of hair, her far from glamorous dressing-gown and her slim bare feet. 'When you're more suitably dressed perhaps you'd like to come and collect the rest of your—er—property.'

The carton of groceries in mind, she said hastily, 'Please feel free to keep it.' From now on she intended to give Fife Cottage a wide berth.

He shook his dark head. 'Though the admiration is mutual, I think not. You see, though I like dogs, night and morning—after a shower, and in the privacy of my own home—I tend to dispense with clothes. . .' He turned, leaving the sentence hanging in mid-air.

His broad-shouldered figure was disappearing through the gate before Angie, who had been standing struck dumb by the graphic picture his last few words conjured up, pulled herself together enough to step back and close the door.

Wiping clammy palms on her dressing gown, she told herself she was an absolute fool to let a perfect stranger affect her like this.

As soon as she'd finished showering she dressed in jeans and a blue and white striped T-shirt and wound her silky ash-blonde hair into a loose coil on top of her head.

Having a clear skin, and brows and lashes several shades darker than her hair, she rarely bothered with make-up, and today was no exception. But it was almost an hour later before, fortified with bacon and egg and several cups of coffee, she set off to collect the bull-terrier.

From being empty, deserted, Fife Cottage now had a lived-in look. The windows were open to the sunshine, and smoke curled lazily from the chimney to hang like a blue-grey genie in the still air.

Adam answered her knock promptly, holding wide the door.

She shook her head primly. 'I won't come in, thank you. I only called for Tosca.'

'So that's her name. Are you an opera buff?'

'Not really, though Simon says...' She stopped speaking abruptly.

Straight-faced, Adam asked, 'What *does* Simon say?'

Ignoring the provocative question, she said over-brightly, 'If you'll get Tosca for me I'll take her out of your way.' When he just looked at her with those extra-ordinary eyes, she found herself babbling, 'I don't really know how you come to have her in the first place.'

'I found her in the living-room last night after you'd gone. Or, to be more accurate, *she* found me. She has a cold, wet nose and an unrestrained curiosity.'

Remembering his unfinished sentence when he'd left her on the doorstep, Angie choked.

'Yes,' he said grimly. 'It came as something of a shock.'

Her sense of humour suddenly getting the better of her, she dissolved into helpless laughter.

Adam's stony-faced disapprobation only served to increase her mirth until, after a moment, he threw in his hand and joined her, his laugh deep and pleasant.

They were still laughing when the blue Mercedes drew up and a blond, well-dressed man jumped out, his handsome face flushed and furious, and came storming up the path.

CHAPTER TWO

SOBERING abruptly, Angie turned to meet the wrath of her fiancé with as much aplomb as she could muster.

'Do you realise just what you've done?' he burst out. 'I had to give Hoskins a sweetener and promise him double time and a bonus on top to get him to come in the first place. Now you've made me look an absolute fool...'

Realising that Adam Langford was listening with sardonic interest, Angie held her own temper in check, and said, 'I'm sorry about that. But perhaps we can discuss it in private.'

Simon, however, seemed oblivious of the other man's presence, and, his smooth, fair face a blotchy red, was into his stride. 'I don't know whether I'll be able to persuade him to come back before Monday. If I can't it will be a total waste of time and money——'

'May I introduce Adam Langford, the Hall's new caretaker?' she butted in determinedly.

This time she got through, and Simon stopped speaking at once, unwilling—as she'd well known—to quarrel in front of a lowly caretaker.

He gave Adam a frosty glance, and, without acknowledging the introduction, seized Angie's arm and hurried her down the path.

Embarrassed by his lack of manners and infuriated by his high-handedness, the minute they were out of sight of the man lounging in the doorway she pulled her arm free and, tight-lipped, led the way back to Clouds.

They had barely reached the long, airy living-room when Simon exploded afresh. 'How could you behave so inexcusably? You know I need a garage before I move in. I refuse to leave my Mercedes standing out in all weathers, and we agreed——'

'That's just it,' she broke in. 'We *didn't* agree. I told you I wasn't prepared to demolish the outhouse until autumn, but you refused to listen.'

'You're being utterly stupid and unreasonable.'

Angie's control snapped and her temper went up like a helium-filled balloon. 'You're the one who's being unreasonable. I'm sure it wouldn't hurt your precious car to stand outside for a month or two.'

'There's no reason why it should have to.'

'There's every reason. As I tried to explain last night, the swallows have eggs and young in their nests.'

'I refuse to have my needs sacrificed for a few dirty birds... If Hoskins had taken no notice of you and obeyed *my* orders——'

'As I made plain to Mr Hoskins, you're not in a position to give orders around here.'

Almost stuttering with rage, Simon began, 'Well, as soon as we're married things will be different, and——'

'Just a minute,' she broke in, her voice dangerously quiet. 'Is that how you see marriage? Being the one to give the orders?'

Alerted by her manner, Simon hesitated, then, his pale blue eyes wary, said, 'Since we've been engaged you've relied on my judgement and... well, someone has to be boss, to give the orders.'

'Let me tell you now that I don't see it that way. Marriage should be an equal partnership, with joint decisions being reached and carried out.'

'So long as those decisions are sensible, but if you're going to let maudlin sentiment get the better of rational judgement—— '

'If by "maudlin sentiment" you mean caring what happens to the swallows——'

'Oh, blast the swallows!' he snapped furiously.

'All you're concerned about is your own convenience.' She flung the accusation at him.

'What I *am* concerned about is not being made to look a fool.'

'Then perhaps you shouldn't have told Mr Hoskins that you owned Clouds.'

Looking distinctly uncomfortable, Simon denied, 'I didn't actually say that. He must have misunderstood me.' Then, in a more conciliatory tone, he went on, 'Look, Angel, all this arguing is most unpleasant, and it's getting us nowhere.'

'You're right,' she admitted. 'I'm sorry, I didn't mean us to quarrel.'

Visibly relaxing, he said magnanimously, 'Well, so long as you're prepared to be sensible we'll forget the whole thing.'

She stiffened. 'By "sensible" you mean...?'

'I mean letting Hoskins make a start without further delay.'

Clearly she told him, 'Mr Hoskins can make a start the moment the last swallow has left, and not a second before.'

The small, satisfied smile died from Simon's lips. 'I don't know what the devil's got into you lately.' With the air of one who was confident he could bring a troublesome subordinate to heel, he cracked the whip. 'I'm beginning to think our engagement was a mistake.'

Riled enough not to consider the consequences, she defied it. 'I'm beginning to agree with you.'

His face livid, Simon spat, 'You're acting like a fool.' Then, swinging on his heel, 'Let me know when you come to your senses.'

A moment later the front door slammed behind him.

Wishing she hadn't made things worse by losing her temper, Angie sighed.

'All in all I thought you were very restrained,' a familiar voice remarked judiciously.

Her head jerked up.

Adam was standing in the back garden, just outside the open casement, sunshine gilding his dark hair, but leaving his lean, arrogant face in shadow.

'Do you make a habit of eavesdropping?' she demanded hotly.

'Your dog wanted to follow you,' he explained blandly. 'So I thought I'd better bring her home. When I realised the—er—discussion was still going on I thought it more tactful to wait.'

'Within earshot, of course.'

'It would have been hard to get *out* of earshot. Neither of you was exactly whispering.'

'That's true,' she admitted stiltedly. 'I'm sorry.'

'I accept your gracious apology.' Before she could react to his needling, he asked briskly, 'Are you going to invite me in, or are you coming out?'

Holding on to her tattered composure with an effort, she asked in a stifled voice, 'What exactly do you want, Mr Langford?'

He came to the open window and rested muscular forearms on the sill. 'As we're going to be neighbours, wouldn't Adam sound friendlier?'

Feeling neither neighbourly nor particularly friendly, she said, 'Very well, Adam.'

'And perhaps I could call you Angela?'

She fell for it. 'You *could*, though that isn't my name.'

He raised winged brows, then gave a sudden chuckle. 'So lover-boy wasn't just trying to be nice when he called you Angel...'

Not for the first time she found herself regretting the name a doting mother had landed her with.

'Well, then, Angel——'

'I wish you'd call me Angie, rather than Angel,' she broke in.

'I'll try,' he assured her mendaciously. 'But I may find the temptation too great. You see, I've never known an Angel before.'

'Look, I'm rather busy,' she remarked pointedly.

'Then we'll get down to business, I understand your stepfather bought some land from the late owner of Wingwood Hall.'

She answered with a cautious, 'Yes.'

'Would you mind showing me where the boundaries run? Chunks of the estate were sold off piecemeal, and one of my first tasks is to check exactly what's left.'

'That seems an odd assignment for a caretaker to be entrusted with.'

'Well, I'm a little more than the Hall's caretaker. Call it a kind of steward for the whole caboodle.'

'Oh.' She didn't know why she was surprised. Thinking about it, neither his manner nor his actions fitted the conventional notion of a caretaker.

'So if you could spare ten minutes or so?' he prodded politely.

'Very well,' she agreed. It was time she took Barnaby his morning treat.

As she went through the kitchen she raided the biscuit tin, and, armed with a handful of ginger-nuts, made her way into the garden, where the cool, sunny air carried the mingled scent of roses and hawthorn blossom.

Tosca came rolling up with her usual bow-legged gait and the flattened ears and crocodile grin she reserved for the times she knew she'd earned a telling-off.

Instead of the anticipated scolding, she was absent-mindedly rewarded with a ginger-nut.

Adam cocked an eye at the biscuits. 'Elevenses?'

Angie shook her head, and, once again made uncomfortably breathless by the nearness of that tall, powerful body, said in a strangled voice, 'They're for Barnaby.'

Her companion fell into step beside her. 'Barnaby? Who's Barnaby?'

'Mr Dawson's goat. He asked me to take care of him, so I put him in with Nicholas. Luckily they get on very well...' There she was babbling again, she thought crossly.

He slanted her a glance. 'Go on, I'll buy it; who's Nicholas?' Then immediately, 'No, don't tell me. Shades of Nicholas Nye! And is he?'

'Is he what?'

'"Lean and grey, lame of a leg, and old"?'

'Yes, he is,' she admitted, surprised that such a masculine man as Adam had so swiftly, and with just a name to go on, picked up the connotation.

She'd had to explain it to Simon. Even then he'd been little wiser, having no liking for poetry and regarding such a taste as effeminate.

As though listening to the echoes of her thoughts, Adam asked, 'So what does the boyfriend think of your tame menagerie? Is it only birds, or animals as a whole, he doesn't care for?'

'He likes animals,' she lied roundly. 'He's very fond of Barnaby.'

'Bully for him.' But it was plain from Adam's sarcastic expression that he wasn't taken in for a moment.

Beyond the smooth green lawns and the bright flower-beds, and the neat vegetable plot which had been Ben's pride and joy, a gate led on to a gently sloping hillside. Off to the right, enclosed by a drystone wall, was a small field with a substantial wooden shed set among bushes of flowering may.

Opening the five-barred gate a crack, Angie slipped inside. When Adam made to follow her, she said, employing the understatement of the year, 'It might be safer to stay where you are. Barnaby can be a bit…aggressive.'

Mr Dawson had used much more down-to-earth language to describe the billy-goat which, when Barnaby was a very young kid, he'd bought in mistake for a nanny.

Adam lifted a dark, curved brow and said easily, 'If Simon likes him, I'm sure we'll get on just fine.'

Cocky devil, she thought sourly.

Barnaby was white, a fine, healthy specimen with a long, silky beard and vicious-looking horns. Head lowered, he took a few menacing steps.

Angie faced him squarely, and for a few moments they eyed each other with mutual respect. Then he came up, and, taking the proffered biscuit from her fingers, crunched with obvious enjoyment.

'An accomplished goat-tamer, I see,' Adam remarked mockingly, and, closing the gate behind him, came strolling over.

Without warning, Barnaby dropped his head and charged.

Adam took a few rapid steps and vaulted the gate, escaping the thrust of those powerful horns with inches to spare.

'An accomplished hurdler, I see,' Angie retaliated sweetly.

Apparently unruffled, he rested his elbows on the top bar. 'You might pass for a lady if it weren't for your impudence.'

'And you might pass for a gentleman if it weren't for your manners.'

After a couple of raps on the wooden gate by way of warning, Barnaby returned to nudge Angie into parting with the rest of the ginger-nuts.

She fed him calmly. Then, being human enough to want to rub in her advantage, she complacently scratched his head.

Like a large, shaggy dog he followed her back to the gate. 'Dare you open it?' she asked Adam in dulcet tones. 'Or shall I climb over?'

A dangerous gleam in his eye, he said, 'If you put your arms around my neck I'll lift you over.'

Angie stepped back hastily.

Adam laughed, white teeth gleaming, deep creases forming at the corners of his well-shaped mouth. 'Well, at least I've discovered one animal you seem to be afraid of.'

Opening the gate, she sidled quickly past him. 'I'm not afraid of you, if that's what you're implying,' she snapped.

One warm hand closed around her bare elbow, preventing her escape, while the other tilted her chin. 'Aren't you, now?'

Standing as though paralysed, she gazed up at him, her golden eyes huge behind the owlish glasses.

Looking down at the heart-shaped face surrounded by wisps of pale, silky hair, the wide mouth above a cleft chin, the nose that had more character than beauty, Adam thought he'd never seen anything more enchanting.

By right of conquest, he bent his dark head and his mouth brushed hers in the briefest of kisses.

That sensuous, thistledown touch was devastating. Simon's most prolonged, passionate kisses had never affected her this way, never left her limp and shaking and made her feel faint.

'You're trembling,' Adam remarked.

The satisfaction in his voice acted like a dose of smelling-salts.

Somehow she stepped back and, doing her best to retrieve the situation, corrected huskily, 'Shivering. I could have done with a jacket.' Then, with determined nonchalance, 'It's been a cold summer up to now, wouldn't you agree?'

'I'm afraid I can't give an opinion about that. I've been living in Australia.'

So that accounted for the faint drawl she'd noticed.

With no change of tone, he added, 'Would you like to go back for a woolly before we venture any further?'

Shaking her head, she said, 'I'll be fine so long as we keep moving.'

As they walked up the slope she kept a good foot of space between them and, refusing to admit to a burning curiosity about this man, chose what she told herself was a safe topic of conversation. 'You're not Australian?'

'No, I'm English born and bred.'

'How long were you down under?'

'Ten years.'

'Which state?'

'I started off in Queensland then moved to South Australia.'

'Have you a . . . a family over there?'

'Now there's a leading question if ever I heard one.'

She felt her cheeks grow hot. 'I didn't intend to pry. I just meant are you home for good or . . . ?'

'Or have I a wife to go back to? Well, if you'd really like to know——'

'I wouldn't,' she denied hurriedly. 'I've no interest whatsoever in your marital status.' And was aware as she spoke that it wasn't the truth.

To her chagrin, he knew it too.

'You're lying through your teeth,' he charged pleasantly.

'What makes you think I'd lie about a thing like that?'

He grinned. 'A knowledge of women. And, to set your mind at rest, I'm not married . . .'

'To set my mind at rest . . . !' Realising she was rising nicely to his bait, she stemmed the heated words, and pointed out with calm reasonableness, 'I'll shortly be married myself.'

He gave a disgusted snort. 'If you've no more sense.'

'What do you mean by that?' she demanded.

'Exactly what I say.'

Biting her lip, she decided to let it go; she'd done more than enough arguing for one day. Her aim should be to get this awkward expedition over as swiftly as possible and see the back of her disturbing new neighbour.

They breasted the slight incline in silence and stood looking across gently rolling parkland dotted with trees standing in their own shade.

Less than half a mile away Wingwood Hall's jumble of gables and tall chimneys stood out against a cornflower-blue sky.

Closer at hand a wide but shallow river meandered along, dividing to make a grassy island on which stood a round white gazebo. From when she was a child Angie had been fascinated by the old place, loving it second only to Clouds.

When Ben had acquired the parcel of land which included the island her joy had known no bounds. She'd happily depleted her small bank balance having the semiderelict summer-house repaired and painted.

'So how much land did your stepfather buy?' Adam's crisp voice broke into her abstraction.

'The strip between our cottage and the river, including the island,' she answered, and felt the man beside her stiffen.

Glancing at him, she saw his face held fury, and something else she couldn't define. Pain, perhaps?

She was wondering what had caused such raw emotion when abruptly it was gone, masked by a determinedly calm interest.

Stepping forward, she pointed. 'The northern boundary runs just this side of the beeches, and the southern along by the sunken fence.'

'Have you access to the island?' His tone was clipped, belying the casualness of his stance.

'By stepping-stones. There used to be a tumbledown wooden bridge on the far side, but it was cleared away when the gazebo was repaired.'

Frowning, he muttered, 'Why in heaven's name did your stepfather want the island and the gazebo?'

'He bought it for me, as an eighteenth-birthday present.'

Adam stood stock-still, as though struck, then his voice, gruff, commented, 'An odd kind of present, surely?'

Angie shook her head. 'Ben knew I'd prefer that to any sports car...'

Adam turned and looked at her. Flustered by those amazing eyes, she went off at a tangent. 'He bought Paula a Porsche...'

'His own daughter?'

'Ben had no children of his own. Paula was his other stepdaughter.'

'But not your sister?'

'No. It's a bit complicated... You see, Ben married twice, each time to a widow with a young child. After a couple of years his first wife went off with another man, leaving him with Paula.

'Ten years later he met and married my mother. I was three at the time; Paula was nearly fifteen.'

'A big age-gap,' Adam commented.

'We never really got to know each other. Paula left home the day she came of age. She loved the bright lights and wanted to be a model.'

'Did she succeed?'

'Yes, she's right at the top of her profession. Almost every week her face appears on the front cover of some glossy magazine.'

'Are you perhaps a tiny bit jealous?'

Angie looked startled. 'No. Even if I had the looks and figure, that kind of life wouldn't appeal to me. What made you think——?'

'I gathered from your tone that you feel resentful towards her.'

Her cheeks turning pink, Angie said, 'I didn't mean to sound like that.' Then, with innate honesty, 'But I *do* feel angry with her. Towards the end I rang to let her know how ill Ben was, but she never came to see him. Not once. She said she was too busy...' Swallowing hard, she added bleakly, 'She didn't even come to his funeral.'

'I'm sorry,' Adam said quietly.

Not altogether sure whether he was apologising for his remark about jealousy or commiserating with her, she said nothing.

After a pensive silence, he asked, 'What happened to your mother?'

'She died when I was twelve.'

'Tough.'

'I missed her dreadfully. But Ben was wonderful to me. He knew how I felt and somehow made my grief bearable.'

An edge of bitterness to his voice, Adam remarked, 'You were lucky to have a father who understood and really cared.'

'In some ways I think he missed her even more than I did. Although she was his second wife, he told me she'd been the one real love of his life. After her death he only went on holiday once. And that was for my sake. He always used to say her spirit lived on in the cottage, and he was at his happiest there with her.' Angie's golden eyes glistened with tears. 'Over the years we grew very close.'

'And he bought you a gazebo.'

Wondering at Adam's strange tone, she explained, 'I'd always loved the place. I used to sit on the riverbank for hours on end and weave stories around it . . .'

'So in spite of your fighting spirit you're a romantic, a dreamer of dreams,' he remarked a shade cynically. 'I should have guessed as much.'

Annoyed that she'd let her tongue run away with her and revealed so much of herself, she turned on her heel and began to walk back to the house.

The man by her side appeared to be lost in thought, and the short journey was completed in silence.

Tosca, who'd been basking idly on the lawn, rose to meet them, her thin tail flicking backwards and forwards with the precision of a metronome.

Just as Adam bent to fuss her, she pricked up her ears and barked. A moment later Angie heard the sound of a car approaching and stopping outside.

Simon. Simon had come back. Relief and another feeling she tried not to recognise mingled.

Accompanied by Adam, she hastened round the side of the house and down the drive, Tosca bounding ahead.

But instead of a blue Mercedes, a bright red sports car was drawn up by the gate. From it was emerging a tall, slim woman, strikingly dressed in navy and white, with short black hair cut in the latest style and the kind of vibrant beauty that could have launched a thousand ships.

'Keep away from me, you brute,' this vision said sharply, and the bull-terrier, who had gone wagging to greet her, retreated to a safe distance.

'Paula!' Angie exclaimed. 'What brings you here?'

'Just passing through, Sister, dear.' Paula sounded dismissive, her attention caught and held by the dark, devilishly attractive man who was standing surveying her with such easy arrogance.

'*Top Fashion* magazine have an afternoon photography session in the gardens of Rydal Castle. All a bit of a bore, really.'

'Will you be staying for lunch?' Angie asked.

'No time, I'm afraid.' Her blue eyes still fixed on Adam with avid interest, as though assessing the sexual promise implicit in the long, mobile mouth, the curiously vital hands, the powerful body, Paula sounded regretful. 'But do introduce me to your friend,' she added.

'This is Adam Langford, my next-door neighbour,' Angie said flatly.

'How nice to meet you.' Her voice a purr, Paula extended a slender, scarlet-tipped hand.

Adam took it. 'And you're Paula.'

'Paula Pleydell.' She gave him a bright, almost challenging look, before remarking, ostensibly to Angie, 'I shall be in town overnight.'

'If you want to stay here...' Angie offered.

'I'm already booked into the Menton Hotel,' Paula said. Then, with a meaningful glance at Adam, 'Though I'm not averse to a little company... Well, I must be off.'

As she slid long, elegant legs into her car, she asked Angie casually, 'I take it your wedding date hasn't been altered?'

So *that* was the reason for Paula's unexpected visit. 'No,' Angie answered briefly.

'Well, as I said, I won't be able to be there, but I expect to be seeing you.' As she spoke the last few words her eyes travelled over Angie's head to the tall, broad-shouldered man standing behind.

Angie watched the car disappear down the track, shocked by the anger and resentment she felt. But she couldn't be *jealous*, she told herself sternly, as they made their way round the back once more. Adam Langford was nothing to her.

At the kitchen door she stood poised, waiting for him to take his leave. When he showed no signs of departing she remarked, 'Well, it's just about lunchtime and I'm getting hungry.'

'So am I,' he agreed in a heartfelt voice.

Opening the door into the comfortable, homely room with its flower-strewn curtains and glowing range, she said firmly but dismissively, 'Well, as you haven't had a chance to shop, I'll get you some——'

'Thanks,' he broke in easily, following on her heels. 'That's kind of you.'

She'd been going to say, Some cheese or something.

Before she could find her voice, he went on, 'Even if I had food in, I dislike eating alone, so I appreciate your hospitality.'

Angie was forced to stay silent, her natural good manners making it impossible to correct his mistake.

Or was it a mistake?

She caught a swift, unholy gleam in his eye which suggested it wasn't. The next second it had vanished, making her wonder if she'd only imagined it.

Stiltedly she said, 'I was intending to have an omelette with green salad.'

'Fine by me,' he assured her cheerfully. Then, as she produced lettuce and watercress and began chopping fresh herbs, 'Mind if I look around?'

A slight sting in her voice, she offered, 'What do you say to a self-conducted tour of Clouds in exchange for showing me the Hall?'

'Done!' he agreed at once, adding in a surprised tone, 'Haven't you ever been inside?'

She shook her head, then admitted ruefully, 'Perhaps it's too much to ask. Mr Dawson always swore it was more than his job was worth to sneak me in.'

'Oh, I think it can be arranged,' Adam said coolly.

As he vanished, she called herself all kinds of a fool. Not only had she been manipulated into giving him lunch, but, without *thinking*, she'd set up a further meeting.

No man had ever affected her so strongly and, re-senting the way he made her feel both agitated and vul-nerable, she should be avoiding him at all costs. He was more in Paula's league.

This reflection did nothing to cheer her.

She was turning the second puffy golden semicircle on to a plate when he reappeared in the doorway.

Obscurely annoyed by such impeccable timing, she waved him to a place set at the stripped-pine table.

He waited until she was settled opposite before taking his own seat, remarking as he did so, 'This is a beautiful old place.'

Picking up her knife and fork, she replied coolly, 'I think so.'

Though he ate with a healthy appetite and obviously enjoyed the simple meal, Adam's table manners were quietly elegant, cancelling out her earlier impression that he was a rough diamond.

Tough he most certainly was, but rough he was not. In fact he was smooth, not with the carefully cultivated polish that was Simon's hallmark, but with the smooth abrasiveness of pumice-stone.

For a while they continued to eat in silence, then, glancing up, he asked, 'What did your stepfather do?'

'He was a well-respected crime-writer.' She smiled fondly. 'That's his desk in front of the living-room window. Despite all the mayhem and murder he wrote about, he was the kindest, most gentle of men, with a real reverence for life.'

'What name did he write under?'

She told him.

'Ah, yes,' Adam said at once. 'I know and like his work, and what you've just described comes through very strongly in his stories.'

Absurdly pleased by that quiet commendation, she said with undisguised pride, 'A lot of people enjoy his books, and he enjoyed writing them. He never made a fortune, and what he did earn he spent on other people, but he was happy...'

Without knowing why, she told him what she'd never told another living soul. 'I sometimes get the feeling Mum and he are both still here, together.'

There was a drifting silence; then, Adam's handsome eyes raking her face, he asked, 'How long is it since he bought the land and the gazebo?'

'Four years.'

A tightness about his well-cut mouth, he asked, 'Did he make the original offer?'

Uneasily aware of the dark thread of bitterness running through the question, she said, 'I don't really know. I believe he was approached by Sir Charles Wingwood.' Then, bluntly, 'Why do you ask?'

'Because it was a sale that should never have gone through.' Adam spoke brusquely, with unnerving authority.

'You mean it wasn't legal?'

'It was legal enough...' he admitted.

With an inward sigh of relief, she removed the empty plates and produced a home-made apple pie and some Stilton cheese.

'But morally wrong of my...the old man to start selling off bits of the estate.'

'Perhaps he had no option,' she suggested, spooning coffee into the percolator. 'A lot of old families have become impoverished. I feel sorry for the new heir. Simon says he'll be faced with crippling death duties and will probably have to sell the place.'

'I take it he's looking forward to handling the sale.'

Flushing a little at the caustic tone, Angie replied coldly, 'If he is, he hasn't said so.'

Not until he was drinking his coffee, which he took black and sugarless, did Adam break the ensuing silence to remark politely, 'Thank you, that was a most enjoyable meal. Your future husband will appreciate having a wife who can cook.'

She shook her head. 'Simon wants to hire a cook-housekeeper.'

Adam looked surprised, then conceded, 'Well, I suppose if you're working...'

'I've already given up my job. He doesn't want me to work.' Awkwardly, she tried to explain. 'You see, it would reflect badly on him if any of his clients came into the library and saw his wife working there.'

'In whose opinion?'

'Well...his.'

Adam's look said it all. 'So what will you find to do all day?'

'I'm not sure,' she replied uncertainly. 'Of course, Simon will need to entertain a great deal...'

'A full-time hostess... How fulfilling. I'm sure you must think yourself very lucky.'

Roused by the undisguised scorn in his voice, she turned on him furiously. 'Any woman would think herself lucky to get Simon. He's handsome and ambitious, he knows exactly what he wants from life, and he's on the way to getting it. He's clever and——'

'Oh, I'm quite sure he's that,' Adam broke in, managing to make his agreement sound far from complimentary. 'He's also a weakling.'

'How dare you call Simon a weakling?' she choked. 'He's nothing of the kind.'

'On second thoughts, that might be true. When it comes to getting his own way he's neither feeble nor ineffectual... Are you going to go crawling back to him? Sacrifice your principles along with the swallows?'

When she didn't immediately answer, Adam remarked with worrying shrewdness, 'He sounded fairly confident you would. Has he any grounds for such confidence? Are you *so* desperate for this marriage to go through?'

Knocked off balance, she stammered, 'W-well, I...'

Adam's face darkened. 'I *see*...'

'You don't see at all,' she dissented angrily. 'And, in answer to your question, no, I'm not going to sacrifice either my principles or the swallows.' Almost to herself, she added, 'I've just got to think of some way round this impasse.'

Sounding angry in his turn, Adam demanded, 'Why? Tell me why.'

When she stayed stubbornly silent, he said impatiently, 'Surely you're not so besotted that you can't see what he's like, see that he's absolutely the wrong man for you?'

'How can you say that? You don't know either of us well enough to pass an opinion.'

'I know a basic, grass-roots difference when I see one. You're a dreamer who loves animals and nature, who enjoys living in the country. He's a selfish b...' Adam stopped, then, choosing his words with more care, went on, 'He's self-orientated, a businessman who has scant regard for nature and hates the country.'

'If you think he hates the country why do you suppose he's agreed to live at Clouds?'

'Possibly until he can get you to agree to sell it?'

'Oh, no!' she denied forcefully. 'He knows how much it means to me, how much it meant to Ben to keep it in the family. He would never put pressure on me to part with it.'

Adam raised his eyes to heaven. 'For God's sake, don't be so naïve. He's an estate agent, isn't he? And this place is an absolute jewel. Use your brains. Didn't you get the distinct impression that he already regards it as *his*?'

His question was too close to the bone, too near to what she herself had been thinking. White to the lips, she cried, 'You're utterly despicable. Get out and stay out.'

Without another word, Adam rose and left by the back door.

Her hands clenched tightly together, Angie waited for the red-hot rage to subside a little. When it did, she felt battered and bruised, totally disorientated, like a survivor from some disaster.

She didn't want to believe Adam Langford. The trouble was, she admitted, her confidence had been badly shaken over the past few weeks.

Simon's behaviour had been so out of keeping with the kind of man she'd first thought him to be. He'd shown a side of his nature that she hadn't liked at all, a bullying, self-centred determination to rule the roost and have things all his own way.

It had caused her to have serious doubts.

But it was much too late for doubts. In order to keep her home and her promise to Ben, she *had* to go through with this marriage.

Angie was lying in bed that night, awake and restless, when the sound of a car engine being started made her get up and go to the window.

She was just in time to see a pair of red tail-lights disappear down the track in the direction of town.

So Adam had taken up Paula's invitation.

It was a most disturbing thought.

CHAPTER THREE

NOT knowing quite what to do about the rift between Simon and herself, Angie waited in the hope that he would relent and, miraculously, everything would come right.

It proved to be a vain hope, as common sense had insisted all along. For one thing, he would never back down or admit to being in the wrong. For another, he held the whip hand and knew it.

As the week crawled past, she got more and more wound up. There was still no word from Simon, nor had she caught so much as a glimpse of Adam Langford.

For which she was truly thankful, she told herself firmly.

Yet, dark and arrogant, he was never far from her thoughts. He even troubled her dreams. Between the two of them she found herself beset and harassed and, somewhat unfairly, wished all men to hell.

Simon, while willing to spend in order to further his ambitions, had a careful—not to say mean—streak.

Unable to afford the kind of big society wedding that would have improved his status, he'd thought it prudent to spend as little as possible, and had plumped for a quiet register office ceremony followed by a small reception at home.

With this in mind, by the following Saturday Angie had subjugated the garden, cleaned and polished until the house gleamed like a new pin, and filled the freezer with pre-cooked dishes.

After breakfast Sunday morning, restless, needing something to do, she decided to turn out the old, neglected toolshed.

The weather had changed dramatically and the last couple of days had been extremely hot and humid. Perspiring the moment she stepped out of the shower, she pulled a pair of frayed denim shorts over brief panties, and a baggy navy T-shirt over nothing, and, having found the shed key, opened the door and peered into the cobwebby gloom, the bull-terrier at her heels.

Just above head-height a sagging shelf held plant pots, shallow trays, bundles of labels, et cetera, while beneath it a conglomeration of junk—rusty gardening implements, broken deckchairs, a wheel-less barrow and a plastic gnome with a red cap and scarf and a vacant expression—gathered dust.

After snuffling around for a while, pouncing on an inoffensive piece of sacking, and tearing it to shreds, Tosca sneezed twice with great violence and, tail wagging, returned to the garden with the pleased air of one whose duty was well done.

Dragging a rickety pair of steps into place, Angie climbed them and, perched precariously, began to tidy the shelf.

The heat and humidity in the shed was high, and her glasses kept slipping down her nose. Finally she took them off and lodged them carefully between some packets of seeds and a dibber.

She had gathered up, and was rewinding, a loose bundle of twine when a large piece of black fluff fell on to her shoulder.

Before she could brush it away it unfurled eight furry legs and disappeared with great rapidity down the loose neck of her T-shirt.

With a shriek she tore the garment off and threw it
from her, teetering precariously before losing her balance
completely and pitching sideways.

Strong arms and a muscular torso abruptly halted her
fall. Adam gave a little grunt as he took her full weight
on his chest, but he didn't even stagger.

All the breath knocked out of her, Angie lay gasping
in his arms. It was several seconds before she became
aware that he was admiring her bare 36C bust with absorbed interest.

'Well, well, well...' he murmured. 'Dressed, you
appear to have a boyish figure...'

Pink and panic-stricken, she tried to wriggle free,
crying hoarsely, 'Put me down!'

Without undue haste he set her gently on her feet and
stepped back.

She wanted to make a run for it, but he was standing
between her and the door. Her arms crossed protectively
over her flattened chest, she looked around frantically
for the discarded T-shirt.

'Lost something?' he queried.

'I took my shirt off...'

Nodding sagely, he agreed, 'Well, it's a very warm
day.'

'It was nothing to do with the day; it was the spider.'

'That sounds like a conundrum,' he remarked, adding
meditatively, 'As a boy I used to enjoy conundrums.'

In a goaded voice, she said, 'I'd be glad if you'd save
your childhood reminiscences for a more appropriate
time.'

He managed to look injured. 'Is that all the thanks I
get for fielding you so neatly?'

Though his face was straight, it was clear that the brute
was enjoying himself. Tendrils of pale, silky hair escaping from the knot on top of her head, she glared at
him like a latter-day Medusa.

'Is this what you're looking for?' He reached into the nearest dark corner and retrieved her T-shirt. Then, apparently deciding he'd teased her enough, he draped it tastefully over a hoe and turned to go, saying over his shoulder, 'I'll wait for you outside.'

When she'd gingerly examined the garment and given it a thorough shake, she put it back on and, having retrieved her glasses, followed him wrathfully.

He was wearing hip-hugging jeans and a black sleeveless vest that showed off his smooth, muscular shoulders. His expression bland to the point of smugness, he lay stretched with easy grace on the sunlit lawn, the epitome of long-legged, masculine superiority—which did precisely nothing for her temper.

Hands on her hips, she marched across and stood over him. 'Are you quite satisfied?'

'Yes, thank you.' His slight Australian drawl evident, he added, 'They're not whoppers, but pretty and firm and a beautiful shape. I've never particularly gone for size myself...' When she choked, he asked innocently, 'Or isn't that what you meant?'

Scarlet as the big velvet poppies in the border, she said, 'No, that isn't what I meant. You know perfectly well it...' She broke off, the little smile tugging at his lips warning her she was playing right into his hands.

Propped negligently on one elbow, he patted the grass between himself and Tosca. 'Do sit down.'

She was about to refuse sharply when she realised her stance gave him the perfect opportunity to study the slim length of her legs, and subsided abruptly.

Calmly he added, 'There's no need to look so embarrassed; I've seen far more on some Oz beaches.'

The assurance did nothing to smooth her ruffled feathers. 'You seem to make a habit of sneaking up on me,' she accused vexedly.

He glanced at her, brilliant, long-lashed eyes narrowed against the sun. 'Not at all. I saw the shed door open, and as I'd come looking for you...'

'Why did you come looking for me?' she wondered aloud, recalling the acrimonious way they'd parted the previous weekend.

Picking up the nuances in the question, he said, 'You mean, if I was going to come why didn't I come sooner?'

'All right, why didn't you?'

'I've been in London all week.'

'With Paula?' The words were out before she could prevent them.

With a glinting look, he suggested, 'Jealous?'

Horrified to find she was, she hastened to say, 'Certainly not!'

He smiled at her vehemence, before continuing casually, 'Now I'm having a day off, so I thought you might like to see over the Hall.'

Excitement stirred, and before her brain could enumerate all the reasons for refusing Angie's treacherous tongue had answered, 'Yes, I'd love to.'

Fool! she berated herself silently. She'd seemed quite unable to keep her cool where he was concerned, and he'd shown himself more than capable of taking advantage of that fact. Every meeting so far had been either uncomfortable, humiliating, or both.

But he was saying, 'Good. I thought as it's such a nice day we might walk over and take a picnic to eat in the gardens.'

Making an effort to retrench, she informed him hastily, 'Well, I mustn't be too long. I have lots to do.'

His clear eyes ironic, he drawled, 'Really?'

Just the one word made her inwardly squirm. But it served her right! she admitted crossly. She ought to know by now that he wasn't easily fooled.

Cheeks flushing with a new surge of colour, she scrambled to her feet. 'I'll get changed, and then make some sandwiches.'

'The food's all taken care of.' As he spoke he retrieved a dark green rucksack from the shade of a bush, settling it on his back. 'And you look fine as you are... Shall we go by way of the island?'

She nodded, and, having shut Tosca in the kitchen, much to the bull-terrier's disgust, joined him.

He walked easily and lightly, neither dawdling nor rushing. Angie often had to trot to keep up with Simon, who considered it manly to stride out, but Adam's un-hurried pace suited her and she enjoyed the short trek to the river.

The grey stepping-stones were dry and polished, the clear water pouring between them with a smooth rush. On the green knoll the gazebo waited, quiet, serene, a little secretive.

Seeing Adam's attention was focused on it with almost painful intensity, Angie asked, 'Do you want to see inside?'

He made no answer.

Thinking he hadn't heard, she was about to repeat the question when he looked at her with blank eyes, then abruptly shook his head.

Now there was no longer a bridge spanning the second fork of the river, they had to wade across. When they'd taken off their sandals, Adam rolled up his jeans and held out a strong brown hand.

Feeling the most absurd sense of panic, she hesitated before reluctantly taking it. As his cool, firm fingers closed around hers she went weak at the knees.

God help her if he ever made a determined pass, she thought feverishly. Faced with such an overpowering physical attraction, she wouldn't stand an earthly.

Sun fell hot on her shoulders, icy-cold water swirled around her slender calves, and beneath her feet the bed of the river was smoothly cobbled and treacherously slippy, but all she was really conscious of was the hand holding hers.

As soon as they reached the grassy bank she pulled free with a profound relief.

When they'd replaced their sandals they made their way across the park and approached Wingwood Hall through formal gardens where the yew hedges needed clipping and weeds forced themselves between the flagstones.

Close at hand the years of neglect became depressingly apparent. Roof tiles were missing and some of the ancient leaded panes cracked. But the old place had weathered centuries of vicissitudes. With its mellow, creeper-covered walls and mullioned windows, its air of *belonging*, it nestled and slept in the sunshine like a contented babe.

Leaving his rucksack on the threshold, Adam unlocked the heavy oak door and ushered Angie into a stone-flagged hall patterned with lozenges of light from the long windows above the staircase.

Gazing up at the great raftered ceiling, she asked, 'Do you know how old the house is?'

'Tradition has it that the original Hall was built in 1492, the year Columbus discovered the New World. In those days there was only one huge living-room, and separate stone staircases led from it to four of the five upper rooms.

'Of course it's been greatly altered and extended since then, though with only ten bedrooms it's still small as stately homes go.'

As, his face curiously set and sombre, he led the way through handsomely proportioned rooms and passages, she saw that, though nothing could spoil the Hall's timeless beauty, damp and decay had wreaked havoc.

Fine plaster ceilings were stained and crumbling, the once elegant wallpaper mildewed and peeling. Curtains, carpets and dust-sheeted furniture smelled musty, and fallen soot and debris lay in the wide stone fireplaces.

The library, with its thousands of mouldering books, almost reduced her to tears.

'A lovely old place like this ought to be lived in and looked after,' she said sadly.

Adam frowned. 'I hope it will be one of these days. Though Sir Charles only died last year, several decades of neglect mean there's a great deal to do.'

'It's such a *shame*.'

'It's a crime,' Adam denounced curtly. 'The old devil has a lot to answer for.'

'Perhaps it wasn't his fault,' she suggested. 'Maybe lack of money or——'

'Try high living in London and compulsive gambling. Over the years, to pay his gaming debts, he sent practically everything of value in the Hall to Sotheby's. Then he started selling the land; may he rot in hell! I've no doubt he'd have sold the house and the inner park if it...' As though regretting his outburst, he broke off abruptly.

There'd been so much black bitterness in his face and voice that Angie bit her lip and said nothing further.

When they were outside once more, his expression lightening, he indicated a high brick wall with a small door set in it and suggested, 'Shall we picnic in the Elizabethan garden?'

Following a paved path winding between overgrown borders rioting with scent and colour, they came to a sun-warmed stone bench. There Adam unpacked the contents of his rucksack—chicken legs, crusty rolls, a carton of mixed salad, cheese, fresh fruit and a flask of coffee.

They ate with their fingers, like children, and Angie smiled inwardly to think how horrified Simon would be if he could see them.

Fingers greasy, she pushed her glasses up the bridge of her nose with the side of her hand, and, recalling an earlier train of thought, queried, 'I suppose you have some connection with the Wingwood family.'

'Yes,' he answered shortly. 'Why do you ask?'

'You're familiar with the Hall... And it's hardly likely that you'd have come all the way from Australia to take a job as steward unless there *was* a connection. Simon says...' She broke off, cursing her unruly tongue.

Adam grinned sardonically. 'What *does* Simon say?'

'Nothing,' she denied hurriedly, helping herself to an apple.

Studying her half-averted face, the tiny golden hairs on her peach-like skin, the faint dew of perspiration, he queried, 'I take it you and he haven't yet made it up?'

About to tell him to mind his own business, she caught the undercurrent of genuine interest in his question, and admitted in a small voice, 'No.'

'So what are you going to do?'

'I just don't know. If it was *anything* but the swallows...'

'You'd give in and let the selfish swine walk all over you.'

'You don't understand...' Her despair was evident.

'No, I don't. Do you want to try telling me?'

She shook her head. 'It's no use...'

His mouth firmed, but to her relief he didn't press her.

Collecting herself, she asked over-brightly, 'What are your plans for the estate?'

Accepting the change of subject with good grace, he answered, 'There's a lot of old timber needs to be cut and fresh trees planted. That done, I'd like to develop the farming side, perhaps run one of the special breeds of sheep...'

Interested, Angie forgot her decision to keep the outing short, and it was almost three-thirty before they started for home, this time crossing the river by way of the stone bridge.

'I once met Lady Wingwood here,' Angie remarked as they joined the track leading to the cottages. 'She was riding a beautiful chestnut mare. Though I was only about nine at the time, I've always remembered how nice she was. She asked my name and where I lived, then told me her name was Elizabeth and she lived at the Hall.'

'Can you recall what she looked like?' Adam asked, his voice curiously brittle.

'She was slim, with dark hair and lovely eyes,' Angie said immediately. 'I thought she seemed sad.'

He made no comment, and, fearing he might be bored by her childhood reminiscences, she lapsed into silence.

But it was too late. A quick glance showed that Adam had been transformed from an outgoing companion into a dark, brooding stranger.

When they reached Clouds she asked a shade hesitantly, 'Would you like some tea before you go?'

'Please.' He seemed to give himself a mental shake, and, dropping into one of her canvas garden chairs, watched with a smile the bull-terrier's exuberance on being released from the confines of the kitchen.

When the tea was made, Adam accepted the proffered mug with a word of thanks and drank in silence. As soon as it was empty he put it down by his feet and said with quiet intent, 'I won't beat about the bush. I'd like that piece of land your stepfather acquired.'

In the most reasonable voice she could muster Angie asked, 'Is there any point in having that back if the whole estate might end up being sold?'

'Contrary to what your fiancé seems to think, it won't. For one thing, it's entailed... So what do you say?'

'I don't want to part with it. In any case, it's not really mine until...'

'Until what?'

She shook her head, repeating stubbornly, 'I don't want to part with it.' Then, in an attempt to divert him, 'You said other chunks of the estate had been sold?'

'That's right, but I especially want...' He hesitated.

'The island?' she suggested, remembering the anger and pain on his face when she'd first told him the island had been included in the deal.

Eyes hooded, lips a thin line, he nodded.

'Why?'

'I have strong personal reasons.'

'Well, as you already know, I have strong personal reasons for wanting to keep it, and——' The shrill chirp of the phone cut through her words. With a muttered, 'Excuse me,' she went through the open door and picked up the kitchen extension.

'Where on earth have you been?' a petulant voice demanded. 'I've been trying to get you all afternoon.'

'Simon!' she exclaimed.

As though making an effort to sound pleasant and conciliatory, he remarked, 'I've missed you.'

Relief made her say what she knew he was waiting to hear, 'I've missed you too.' As she spoke she watched Adam's tall, well-knit figure head towards the side-gate.

'Don't you think it's about time we stopped this silly feud?'

Dragging her mind back to Simon, she agreed, 'Yes, it's high time.'

'I thought a week should be long enough to bring you to your senses.'

His satisfaction jarred, but she bit her lip and said nothing.

'Have dinner with me tomorrow night and we'll let bygones be bygones and settle the rest of the wedding plans.'

'What's wrong with tonight?'

'You know I don't care for eating out on a Sunday evening. Besides, I've a business appointment shortly and I'm not sure what time I'll be free.'

Aware that he sometimes saw his more important clients over the weekend, she gave in with good grace. 'All right, tomorrow night.'

'Shall we say seven o'clock at Macey's? And I'll ring Hoskins and give him the go-ahead to start first thing in the morning.'

'No!'

Almost incredulously, he said, 'You're not still refusing to have that eyesore knocked down?'

'Only until the swallows have gone. You don't know how much it means to me... I can't bear to think of the eggs and babies being destroyed... Please, Simon,' she begged, 'let me have my way in just this one thing and I promise I won't ask——'

'Surely you don't imagine I'm going to back down now for such stupid sentimentality?' he broke in furiously. 'I've told Hoskins the job *will* go ahead, and I refuse to be made to look foolish again... Now, for the last time, are you prepared to let the builders make a start?'

'No, I'm not.'

'Then our engagement's over,' he snarled. 'Find yourself someone else to marry.'

'I might just do that.' With a shaking hand she slammed the receiver down.

'Oh, *hell*!' she muttered. Now what was she going to do?

'Don't be in too much of a hurry, lass...' Ben's words when she'd told him Simon had proposed came back to her. 'Not unless you really love him.'

'Oh, I *do*,' she'd said eagerly.

'Well, if you're certain he's the man for you...'

But though Ben had been trying hard to sound cheerful, she'd known him well enough to be aware that, much as he wanted to see her safely married, he'd had grave doubts.

At that time she'd had none. She'd been happy to think that her future, along with the cottage, was secure.

Oh, Ben! she cried silently. Only Ben was gone, and the future in ruins.

To have any chance of rebuilding that future she needed a husband. And quickly. But she knew so few men, and most of the ones she did know were either much too young or already spoken for...

Angie never knew how long she'd sat there racking her brains when suddenly the idea came. At first she dismissed it as impossible, but it kept stubbornly re-occurring.

It was a chance. Maybe her only chance.

Although she was basically quiet and shy, with a modest opinion of her own worth, Angie had never lacked guts. Now, with the courage of despair, she marched round to Fife Cottage and banged on the door.

It swung open almost immediately, Adam's tall frame filling the doorway. He was still wearing the black sleeveless vest and close-fitting denims.

She looked up at him to find his mouth was hard, his expression bleak, uncompromising; and her throat muscles constricted. 'I...I'd like to talk to you,' she managed.

'Come to tell me you've abandoned your principles and all's well between you and lover-boy?' His dark greeny-blue eyes held hers.

Beautiful eyes in such a tough face, she thought, hating the flicker of contempt she saw in their clear depths.

'No, that isn't what I came to tell you.'

When he merely waited, she added uncertainly, 'I came to *ask* you something. May I come in?'

'Of course.' He moved to one side and ushered her in with exaggerated politeness. 'Do sit down.'

Not sure how much longer her legs would support her, she sank on to the nearest chair, part of her mind registering that the room now looked clean and pleasant, lived in.

He leaned negligently against the mantel, saying nothing, just watching her.

She swallowed hard.

'Well?' he prompted, without impatience. 'What do you want to ask me?'

Staring down at her clasped hands, she blurted out, 'Will you marry me?'

Though she wasn't looking at him, she was aware that he froze. Then, his voice smooth and hard as polished steel, he said, 'Call it pride if you like, but I don't take easily to being second best. And despite the—er—obvious rewards, I can't say I care to fill the role of substitute for lover-boy.'

Colour flaming in her cheeks, she denied, 'I don't want a substitute for Simon. I...I just need a husband.'

Sounding precisely the opposite, Adam said, 'I'm flattered, of course, but...'

She'd been an utter fool to come and lay herself wide open to this kind of humiliation, Angie thought despairingly. Jumping to her feet, she headed blindly for the door.

As she reached it a hand caught her arm in a grip of iron. 'Don't rush off.'

'Let me go,' she spat, trying to pull free.

Adam's hold tightened. 'Having just proposed to me, I really think——'

'I *haven't* proposed to you,' she denied hotly.

'Strange, that's what it sounded like. But if it wasn't a proposal, stay and tell me what it was.'

'It was a stupid idea,' she muttered. 'Forget it.'

'That might not be easy. It isn't every day a woman I scarcely know asks me to marry her.'

'I didn't ask you to marry me.' Seeing his brows shoot up, she admitted, 'Well, I did, but I . . . I didn't mean it.'

'Then perhaps you'd like to explain exactly what you *did* mean.' As he spoke he was towing her back across the room.

Struggling against his hold, she said miserably, 'I just *wish* you'd forget the whole thing.'

He pushed her gently but firmly into a chair. 'I *might*. But first you owe me an explanation.' Taking a seat opposite, he leaned back and, his heavy-lidded eyes fixed on her face, insisted, 'So go ahead.'

After a moment, her voice scarcely above a whisper, she obeyed. 'When Ben first discovered his illness was terminal, he began to worry about his will.'

She paused, then went on doggedly, 'If there'd been any money, he would have left that to Paula and the cottage to me. But there wasn't . . . The three of us got together to discuss it. Paula wanted to put Clouds up for auction and split the proceeds, but——'

'*She* doesn't want the place?' Adam broke in swiftly.

'No,' she hates the country. She has a flat in Prince Regent Mansions, Mayfair.'

He whistled. 'If she can afford that, then surely she doesn't need any of Ben's money?'

'She's always liked an expensive lifestyle...and I suppose no one can blame her for wanting her fair share. But Ben couldn't bear the thought of selling the cottage...' Angie paused to swallow a lump in her throat.

'When he told her that, and declared his intention of willing the place to me, Paula turned really nasty. She said if he did she'd go to court and fight to the bitter end to have the will overturned. The thought of leaving me to face that kind of trouble upset him dreadfully.'

'So what did he do?' Adam probed gently.

'After a lot of thought, he made a will leaving it to the one who married first.'

'That could have been Paula.'

'It *could*; that's why she agreed to it. She said it gave both of us an equal chance. But Ben thought it was much more likely to be me. Paula had always hated domesticity, and the idea of being tied to one man.'

Adam grunted. 'With so much at stake, wasn't there a chance she might change her mind?'

'There was always that chance,' Angie agreed steadily. 'But Ben included the proviso that the newly-weds should live in the cottage for at least a year.'

She sighed. 'He's done all he could, and I promised him I'd do everything *I* could to make sure Clouds was safe.'

'I see,' Adam said slowly. 'So that's why lover-boy was taking to a country life. I didn't think it was his scene.'

'He agreed quite readily to live there——' Angie began stiffly.

'Until the year was up and he could get his hands on the place.'

'If he was marrying me just to get his hands on the cottage, why did he refuse to give way over the outhouse?'

'Because he was confident *you* would.' Watching her like a hawk, Adam went on, 'He must be sure you're fathoms deep in love with him. After all, there's no desperate hurry——'

'That's just it,' Angie broke in, 'there is...'

Adam's expression hardened. 'I see.' His voice icy, he demanded, 'If I'd agreed to marry you, would you have bothered to tell me?'

'Well, of course, though I don't...' She broke off abruptly and jumped to her feet, her face flaming with colour. 'You think I'm pregnant!'

'Aren't you?'

'I most certainly am *not*. You... You...' She spluttered to a halt, unable to think of any suitable scathing adjective. 'Do you really think I'd walk in here and ask you to marry me if I were carrying another man's child?'

Adam had risen to his feet, and when she would have gone storming off he took her shoulders and pressed her back into the chair.

'If you don't want to be misjudged, suppose you tell me exactly what makes matters so urgent that you'll propose to a comparative stranger.'

For a moment outrage vied with reason. Reason won. Sighing, she told him, 'A little over a week ago, quite by chance, I read a magazine article about the country's top six fashion models. Paula was one of them. It mentioned that she'd just have time to fit in an assignment for Paris couturier André Jacques before her August wedding.'

'And she hasn't told you about it?'

Angie shook her head.

Adam's dark brows knitted, then, deciding against mentioning the disquieting thought at this juncture, he sat down again opposite and regarded Angie soberly. 'I take it you told lover-boy about Paula's forthcoming wedding?'

'Yes.'

Adam clicked his tongue. 'That was foolish of you.'

In retrospect Angie could see that it had been. Immediately afterwards, Simon had become even more aggressive and domineering.

After a moment, his expression caustic, Adam suggested, 'Perhaps as a last resort you could try an appeal to his better nature. After all, three months isn't that long to wait for a garage.'

'I've already tried,' she admitted. 'But he doesn't want to look a fool in front of Mr Hoskins. It's a matter of pride now, and he won't change his mind.'

Adam's mouth twisted into the semblance of a smile. 'You mean he thinks he holds all the aces. And perhaps he does. You've given up your job, and in a matter of weeks you may lose your home, unless you're prepared to knuckle under to marry him.'

Angie lifted her chin. 'Now I've found out what he's really like I don't *want* to marry him. And I don't think Ben would want me to.'

'Suppose he *does* change his mind?'

'He won't,' she said with certainty. 'He told me the engagement was over, to find myself someone else to marry.'

'So the situation's difficult.'

'Hopeless,' she corrected.

He shook his head. 'If all you need is another husband... Where's your get-up-and-go?'

She laughed hollowly, and made the hackneyed retort, 'It got up and went.'

'Nonsense,' he said briskly. 'It must have taken a great deal of courage to come round here and ask me to marry you... So suppose you tell me exactly what you have in mind...'

CHAPTER FOUR

ANGIE shook her head and, her voice jerky, begged, 'Forget it, please, it was a ridiculous idea. It would never have worked.'

'Why not?' he asked, his lean face intent, hawklike, full of dark attraction.

Taking off her glasses, she rubbed her eyes. 'I...I hadn't thought it through.'

'Try *talking* it through,' he suggested.

Looking down at her clasped hands, her long, gold tipped lashes brushing her cheeks, she muttered, 'I'd rather forget all about it.'

'Well, I wouldn't.' Both words and tone were uncompromising. 'Look at me, Angel!'

His deliberate use of her given name brought her blonde head up, lashes flickering.

He leaned forward, knees a little spread, bronzed arms resting on denim-clad thighs. Her reluctant gaze was drawn to the strength of his shoulders, his bulging biceps, the light covering of crisp dark hair on his forearms.

Her throat went dry, her palms clammy, and, becoming uncomfortably aware of her own bare legs, she swallowed, wishing fervently that they'd both changed. In the confines of the cottage so much exposed flesh was unnerving, to say the least.

Smiling ironically, as if following her train of thought, he continued with quiet determination, 'My curiosity's aroused. You must know other eligible men, so why *me*? Was it lust at first sight?' He gave her a swift, taunting

glance that made her know what he was remembering
and brought a rush of warmth to her cheeks.

'No, it wasn't,' she denied hurriedly. 'But I thought
I had something you wanted and——'

'You have something *most* men would want.'

Putting her glasses back on, she said stiffly, 'I wasn't
offering myself.'

He raised a dark brow. 'Suppose you tell me what you
were offering and what you expected in return.'

'I wanted a husband...*in name only*,' she added
swiftly, 'for a year.'

'And then what?'

'At the end of a year, a nice quiet annulment. I...I
thought of you because of the land, the island...'

His face a bronze mask, he sat quite still, waiting.

'I would have given it to you.'

'That's very generous,' he said slowly.

'Not really,' she objected. 'I would have been getting
so much more. But as I say, I hadn't thought it through,
considered all the obstacles...'

'The obstacles being?'

'The main one you already know. Under the terms of
Ben's will my...husband would be expected to live at
Clouds with me for twelve months.'

'I can't see that that's insurmountable. After all, I'm
on the spot, so to speak. I could work from your place
just as easily as I can from here. And as I remember it,
there are *three* bedrooms and we wouldn't even need to
share a bathroom... What are the other stumbling-
blocks?'

'Well, I...I...' She floundered and stopped.

'You haven't actually thought of any more?'

'No,' she said, refusing to mention the one that had
just hit her like a brickbat and made a fine dew of perspiration break out on her temples. 'But there's bound
to be some.'

He ran lean fingers over his jaw. 'I can think of one for a start.'

Tawny-gold eyes on his face, she waited uneasily.

'It's a lot to expect of any normal red-blooded man...to live with a beautiful woman and be celibate for a year.'

'No, I...' She flushed a little. 'Well, I wouldn't have expected that.'

Watching her cheeks grow pink, he decided it was sweet amusement to tease her. 'I understood you to say a marriage in name only.'

'Yes, but I...'

'Do you mean this "husband" of yours would have been free to roam? That could create problems."

'Well, I told you I hadn't thought it through. It's a stupid idea.'

'I think, despite some obvious snags, it's quite a good idea. In fact I accept your proposal.'

'You accept?' It came out as a squeak.

'Yes.' He hid a smile, before becoming serious. 'Though I have to point out that you'd be running a big risk. For all you know, I might have nasty habits, or not be clean around the house. I might even take a leaf out of our not so simple Simon's book and try to get my hands on the cottage. You would need to trust me.'

'I do.' And it was the truth. Without really *knowing* him, without any logical reason, she trusted him implicitly. Somewhere in her subconscious she must have been aware of that to have approached him in the first place.

'Well, you *shouldn't* trust me.' His words shook her, as he'd intended them to. 'And I'll tell you why. I'm just a normal, ordinary man...'

The hell he was!

'I'm reasonably tidy and clean around the house. I have no nasty habits...'

Unless you could count walking about with no clothes on!

'I won't attempt to cheat you in any way, and, as a married man—albeit in name only—I won't be doing any roaming. But—and here's the snag—though I'll try, I can't guarantee to regard you as a sister.'

Angie went all over goose-flesh.

Seeing the shiver she was unable to control, he added positively, 'Though I *can* promise that I won't do anything you don't want me to do. What do you say? Is it a deal?'

A clever strategist, he'd put the onus squarely on her. Alarm racing through her, she hesitated.

'What's the matter?' he asked mockingly. 'Aren't you sure you can trust yourself?'

Admitting, to her chagrin, that she was far from sure, she said quickly, 'Of course I'm sure.' Then, feeling an ignoble urge to hit back, she tagged on nastily, 'It must be nice to think you're irresistible.'

He grinned, his ego unscathed. 'So long as *you* don't think so.'

'I most certainly don't.'

Suddenly businesslike, he said, 'Then there should be no real problem, so I suggest you make up your mind as soon as possible.'

'But *you* don't know anything about *me*,' she cried with more than a hint of panic. 'I could be bad-tempered, slovenly, impossible to live with...'

'Are you by any chance trying to talk me out of it?' he asked mildly.

Pulling herself together, remembering what was at stake, she shook her head. 'No, but it's only fair to warn you...'

His eyes glinted green. 'And it's only fair to warn you that I could be the kind of man who would take a bad-tempered, slovenly, impossible to live with woman over his knee.'

When, with little quivers of nervous excitement racing through her, she remained silent, he remarked, his beautiful mouth faintly stern, 'Something struck me earlier when we were talking ... Don't you think it's distinctly odd that Paula, who was quite aware of your wedding date, chose to get married just a week or so *after* you?'

He'd put into words her unspoken worry. 'You think she might be planning to ... ?'

'Deliberately mislead in order to pip you to the post? It did cross my mind.'

'But then she and her husband would have to live at Clouds for a year. I can't see her doing that. Apart from any other consideration, she *hates* the place.'

'Mmm ...' Adam ran thoughtful fingers over his jaw. 'Well, if she's marrying a wealthy man, money might no longer be an object.'

Facing up to the truth, Angie admitted, 'If she was marrying a multimillionaire I'm sure she would still be determined not to lose out.'

Adam grunted. 'Which makes it seem even stranger. So perhaps we should arrange the wedding for as soon as possible.'

With a return of the panic, Angie stammered, 'B-but a year's a long while to be tied. Don't you need some time to think about it? You may change your mind.'

Coolly, he told her, 'I'm not in the habit of changing my mind once it's made up.'

'The island must mean a great deal to you,' she said slowly.

'It does. Though that isn't the only reason. I have another one.'

'Oh?' She waited expectantly.

A little twist to his lips, he said, 'I'll tell you what it is when the year's up.' Then briskly, 'Now go and get changed and I'll take you out for a meal to celebrate our engagement.'

In a state of confusion, she hesitated. Then, thinking how pleased Ben would be, a sudden smile lit up her face, bestowing a breathtaking radiance. 'All right,' she agreed. 'Give me half an hour.'

'Half an hour it is.' Standing in the doorway, he watched her walk down the path, and he was still remembering that smile as she disappeared from sight.

While Angie showered and got ready, she found herself wondering what reason Simon would give his carefully cultivated society friends for breaking off their engagement.

It had come as a shock, but, like a weight lifting from her soul, she knew she was glad he *had* broken it off.

They could never have been happy together.

Though for a long time she'd managed to blind herself to the truth, they were utterly different in attitude and outlook, in their sense of what was important in life.

Pushing thoughts of Simon to the back of her mind, she chose a fine, soft dress patterned with various-coloured anemones on a dark blue background. Against it her hair, which she'd left to curl loosely on to her slim shoulders, looked like pale spun silk.

Judging by Adam's appreciative glance when she opened her door to his knock, he liked what he saw.

'And ready on time too,' he remarked. 'That augurs well for the future.'

Freshly shaved, his dark hair parted on the left and trying to curl, he looked coolly elegant in beige trousers and an olive-green shirt. He was wearing a green and beige striped tie—making her wonder if he was planning to take her somewhere fairly formal—and a light jacket was slung over his shoulder, held by one crooked finger.

It was a very warm evening, the temperature having stayed up in the twenties, and low evening sun still slanted across the green hills and dales. But on the eastern horizon banks of purple and black storm clouds were gathering menacingly.

She hoped it wasn't an omen.

Preceding Adam down the drive, Angie wished he hadn't mentioned the future. She still had to come to terms with what she'd done, stop her heart behaving like a mad thing every time she contemplated living in the same house with so much blatant—if unselfconscious—masculinity.

Waiting outside the gate was a neat white hatchback that looked brand new. He helped her into the car with the impeccable good manners he always displayed, before taking his seat behind the wheel.

Instead of starting the engine, however, he surprised her by asking, 'Did Simon give you an engagement ring? I've never seen you wearing one.'

She shook her head. 'He thought an expensive ring was a waste of money, and he refused to let me wear a cheap one.'

'Oh? And how did you feel about it?'

Under the spell of those fascinating eyes, she found herself admitting, 'A bit disappointed. I'd have been quite happy with something simple and inexpensive.'

Feeling in his pocket, Adam produced a ring and slipped it on to the third finger of her left hand.

In something of a daze she stared down at a huge oval topaz in an antique gold setting. Glowing and flawless, it looked wonderful on her slim but capable hand and fitted as though it had been made for her.

She was wondering how he came to have it when he answered her unspoken query. 'It belonged to my mother.'

'Oh, but I——'

A finger laid on her lips stopped her protest. 'It's only semi-precious,' he went on, 'but it matches your eyes...'

His words, and the touch of that lean finger against her mouth, made her heart start to behave as erratically as a ping-pong ball on a jet of water.

'However, if you don't like it, on Monday I'll take you to choose something different.'

'Oh, I *do* like it... It's b-beautiful,' she stammered. 'But there's no need... I mean, you don't have to give me a ring. It isn't as if this was a real engagement——'

'It may not be *real*,' he broke in, an edge to his voice, 'but surely it has to *appear* so? Or were you planning on telling everyone the whole truth?'

Shrinking at the thought of having to admit that she'd proposed to him, she shook her head dumbly.

'Then I suggest we follow tradition and let everybody believe it was love at first sight.'

'Simon won't believe that.' She spoke without thinking.

Adam's jaw tightened. 'Well, if he's so sure that, despite everything, you still love *him*, you'll have to try and convince him otherwise.

'Or would you prefer to call the whole thing off? Sink your pride along with your principles and beg him to take you back? That's no doubt what he's hoping for.'

Then on a clear note of warning, 'If you want to change your mind say so now; this may be your last chance.'

'I don't want to change my mind.' With that flat statement she burnt her bridges and made reneging impossible. Despite his good manners, his smooth self-control, Adam was formidable, not a man she would care to cross or trifle with.

'In that case, suppose we seal our bargain?' The next moment he had removed her glasses, and his mouth, firm and disciplined, was on hers.

Caught completely off guard, her lips parted beneath the light, but unmistakable, demand of his. Taking immediate advantage, he deepened the kiss. It had the same effect as dropping a lighted match into a box of fireworks.

Mind and body, she went up in a shower of bright sparks and explosive passion, and of their own accord her arms went around his neck, her fingers tangling in the crisp, dark hair curling into his nape.

He was the first to draw back from the conflagration, leaving her deprived and still burning.

She opened dazed eyes. Though his features were slightly blurred, she could see he looked as cool and unmoved as if he'd been saluting a virtual stranger. In fact a stranger might have engendered more warmth, she thought, in no state to notice his quickened breathing or question her own resentment.

Thrown off balance, both by his reaction and her own, it was several seconds before she could speak. When she was able, doing her utmost to hide the devastating effect the touch of his mouth had had on her equilibrium, she demanded acidly, 'Would you kiss your sister like that?'

Replacing her glasses with care, he said, 'I haven't got a sister. I was an only child.'

Dismissing that as irrelevant, she pointed out, 'You promised you would try to regard me as a sister.'

A devilish gleam in his eye, he retorted, 'I also said I wouldn't do anything you didn't want me to do.'

Remembering her ardent response, she was effectively silenced.

Hoping he wouldn't notice the blush mantling her cheeks, she stared straight ahead though the windscreen while he started the engine.

Darfield, though a bustling market town during the week, was relatively peaceful on Sundays. As usual the cathedral close had its share of visitors, and along the river's leafy embankment people were still enjoying the sun, but the streets themselves were almost deserted.

Wondering how well Adam knew Darfield, Angie got ready to give him directions. But, without needing to ask, he headed into the old part of town.

After threading his way though a maze of narrow streets lined with black and white half-timbered buildings, he turned into a picturesque cul-de-sac and drew up outside Carriages.

Part of a converted mews, it was the most exclusive restaurant in town, and Angie wondered uneasily if he had any idea how very expensive it was. She had once mentioned to Simon that for a special treat she'd like to eat there, and he had visibly blenched.

Among the cars already parked on the fine gravel apron were two Bentleys, a Rolls-Royce, and a Mercedes. Drawn up beside them the little hatchback looked incongruous.

Judging that Adam was, in his own way, a proud man, and wary of hurting his feelings, she said carefully, 'This is an awfully posh place, I believe.'

When he continued to look unconcerned, she tried again. 'I should imagine it's necessary to reserve a table in advance, but there's Le Bijou not too far away.'

He raised a dark brow. 'Don't you care for my choice?'

'Oh, yes, but I thought . . .' She stopped, flushing, the ironic gleam in his eyes making it clear he knew exactly what had prompted her objections.

As he opened her door and helped her out he bent his head and murmured quizzically, 'Don't worry, you won't have to wash up.'

Seeing her flush deepen, he touched her hot cheek in a gesture of contrition. 'You've a kind heart, and I'm being a swine to you.'

'You said it.'

He chuckled. 'That's my Angel.'

The oak-beamed restaurant, with its elegant green and gold décor and widely spaced tables, appeared to be full.

Already shrugging apologetic shoulders, the head waiter advanced on them.

Adam murmured a few quiet words in his ear. A banknote unobtrusively changed hands, and in the twinkling of an eye, it seemed, a table and two chairs appeared from nowhere and were set up in a vacant space near one of the windows.

By the time they had been ceremoniously seated, place-settings, sparkling glassware and fresh flowers adorned the green linen cloth. In an instant, gold-tasselled menus were produced and the wine waiter was standing by to take Adam's order of vintage champagne.

'Impressed?' he enquired mockingly, when they were alone.

'Overwhelmed,' she answered truthfully.

'Don't worry, I can pay for it.'

'I'm sure you can. But...' She stopped, biting her lip.

'But you're afraid I might beggar myself?' When she said nothing, he went on mildly, 'As it's a special occasion I thought we could splash out a little.'

As far as she was concerned, vintage champagne was splashing out a lot.

The meal proved to be first-class, and Adam was a stimulating companion, amusing and erudite. She wanted to ask him about himself, but, whether by accident or design, he kept the conversation impersonal and she felt constrained to do the same.

They had reached the coffee stage when, through a screen of plants and foliage, Angie caught a glimpse of a couple who had just come in. The woman, a tall, well-dressed redhead, was accompanied by a slimly built man with fair hair.

The pair, who had evidently not booked, were being turned away when, with the slightest movement of one hand, Adam summoned the head waiter. A low-voiced request sent the man hurrying to the door, and a moment later he returned with the newcomers at his heels.

Adam rose to his feet while Angie sat as though turned to stone. The woman, good-looking in a hard-boiled way, she had never seen before, but the man was Simon, and he was staring at her as if he couldn't believe his eyes.

'Good evening, Perry,' Adam said, a cool air of authority underlying his politeness. 'We wondered if you'd care to join us.'

Clearly both startled and nonplussed, Simon hesitated, his face turning an unbecoming brick-red. Then, realising that his companion was looking at him, he pulled himself together. 'I really don't think——'

'Oh, but we can't refuse such a kind invitation,' she broke in, eyeing Adam with overt interest.

Snapping his fingers, the head waiter sent his minions scurrying for two additional chairs, place-settings, menus and another bottle of Bollinger.

Fully recovered now, Simon cleared his throat and said pompously, 'Mrs Hunter-Gore, I'd like to introduce Miss Doland and Mr Langford...'

Disregarding the quiet girl in the dark-rimmed, owlish glasses, the redhead addressed Adam. 'Langford? I don't know the name, yet I could have sworn we'd met socially.'

Before he could answer, Simon butted in, 'I think you must be mistaken, Mrs Hunter-Gore.' A gleam of pure malice in his pale blue eyes, he added with conscious superiority, 'Mr Langford is the caretaker at Wingwood Hall.'

'Wingwood Hall!' Mrs Hunter Gore exclaimed. 'Now I have it!' Her eyes fixed on Adam, she gushed, 'We met last week in Knightsbridge, at Cynthia Hamilton's party...'

When Adam's expression stayed politely blank, she went on, 'Well, not exactly *met*, you were just leaving as I arrived, but you were pointed out to me... Surely you're Sir Adam Wingwood?'

His annoyance swiftly masked, Adam made a formal little bow of acknowledgement.

'Well, isn't that a strange coincidence!' she exclaimed.

'Strange indeed,' Adam murmured, with a rueful glance at Angie.

Her mouth tight, she refused to look at him. The fact that he was Adam *Wingwood* explained quite a lot of things... But why on earth was he calling himself Langford?

While Simon stood as if rooted to the spot, Adam moved round the table to seat his lady guest, before saying crisply, 'I take it you've had a working weekend, Perry. You must be tired. Do sit down.'

Still looking as if he'd received an unexpected boot in the midriff, Simon obeyed.

As one of the waiters took the newcomers' order, Angie struggled to come to terms with the situation. She felt shaken and angry and somehow *betrayed*. Why had Adam let her make such a fool of herself? Why hadn't he *told* her who he was?

Apparently having been thinking much the same, Simon—at a disadvantage and totally lacking his usual studied smoothness—blurted out, 'If you're Wingwood, why the hell are you calling yourself Langford and living in a caretaker's cottage?'

Adam glanced at Angie, and, as though explaining to her rather than Simon, replied, 'Langford was my mother's maiden name. I've been using it for the past ten years... And as, at the moment, the Hall is scarcely habitable, the cottage seemed preferable.'

Leaning forward eagerly, her sharp brown eyes fixed on Adam, Mrs Hunter-Gore broke into the conversation. 'My husband, who's away on an extended business trip, left it to me to find a decent sized property in the Darfield area. I came up from London specially to look at Belton Manor, but the place is far too dark and cramped.'

When Adam said nothing, merely waited courteously, she gave him a meaningful glance. 'I understand you'll be putting Wingwood Hall up for sale.'

'I'm afraid you've been misinformed,' he told her coolly, waving the wine waiter away and pouring the bubbling champagne himself. 'I've no such intention.'

'But surely the place will need a great deal of money spending on it?'

The implication was quite obvious, and Angie cringed. Mrs Hunter-Gore might be rich, but she could hardly be called well bred.

Controlling the anger that had flared briefly in his eyes, Adam enquired silkily, 'Are you offering to loan me some?'

The redhead was only momentarily disconcerted. Forcing a light laugh, as though they'd both been joking, she asked, 'So are you planning to live there eventually, Sir Adam?'

'I hope so, but it depends on my future wife.' He turned his dark head to smile at Angie.

There was a stunned silence, then Simon and Mrs Hunter-Gore spoke simultaneously.

'You can't mean...!'

'But I was told you'd only recently returned from abroad...'

Ignoring Simon's incredulity, Adam replied blandly, 'From South Australia, to be exact. I met Angel a little over a week ago and, to use a rather trite phrase, fell in love at first sight.'

Reaching over, he lifted Angie's hand to his lips. 'We've just got engaged, hence the celebration.'

Casting a glance at Simon, she saw him goggling at the ring. Despite his unfeeling behaviour, his attempt to put Adam down, she felt sorry he'd learnt the truth like this.

But what was she thinking of? It wasn't the truth. Adam was only playing some kind of game with them all...

Looking at Angie with new respect, the redhead asked a shade acidly, 'And will you be marrying with equal speed?'

Fondling the hand he was still holding, giving a good impression of a man completely besotted, Adam said, 'We will if I have my way. So if you'll excuse us, we have things to talk about, plans to make...'

Signalling the waiter, he paid the bill for four without turning a hair, and adding a handsome tip.

It would serve him right if, in order to make a show, he *had* beggared himself, Angie thought bitterly.

Not having spoken a single word, she found herself being escorted to the door. But she would have plenty to say, she vowed, once they got back.

Outside it was prematurely dark, the sky a sullen mass of charcoal-grey cloud, and in the distance lightning flashed and thunder rumbled menacingly.

She'd been afraid of thunderstorms as a child, until Ben, bless him, had told her that it was only the angels having a fireworks display.

As he started the car Adam remarked, 'I hope meeting Perry and Mrs Hunter-Gore hasn't spoilt your evening.'

'We didn't exactly *meet* them,' Angie pointed out curtly. 'You went out of your way to invite them over.'

After a sidelong glance at her set face, he said unrepentantly, 'It served a useful purpose. At least he now knows the score.'

Though further infuriated by the undisguised satisfaction in Adam's tone, she said merely, 'And so do I.' Then, biting her lip hard, she relapsed into silence. This was no time to start a fight.

Traffic was much thicker now, with families hurrying homewards after a day in the country, and while Adam concentrated on his driving she sat silently stoking the fires of anger and resentment.

As they left the hamlet of Hallfield behind them the storm broke, the first heavy drops of rain spattering on to the windscreen. By the time they turned into the drive at Clouds it was bucketing down and the angels were putting on a spectacular show.

Drawing the car as close to the house as possible, Adam doused the lights and remarked, 'This isn't going to ease off for ages, so I suggest we make a run for it.' He unfastened her seatbelt and, dropping his light jacket around her shoulders, added, 'Give me your key and wait here.'

The man in command, she thought sourly, as she handed him the key.

He sprinted, but in the lightning's glare she could see his shirt was plastered to him before he'd even reached the door.

As soon as he put the key in the lock she jumped out and hurried after him ignoring his instructions. Despite the jacket, she felt the rain wetting her back and shoulders, and they were both soaked to the skin before they'd crossed the threshold, their entrance being impeded by the bull-terrier, who saw no reason to mitigate her welcome.

Standing in the hall drenched and dishevelled, they stared at each other until, after a second or two, Adam burst out laughing.

Normally she would have joined him, but, the devil riding her, she wiped the rain from her glasses and said sharply, 'I'm glad you think it's funny.'

'If you could see your face! You look as cross as the Hobgoblin of Rantipole Wood. I can understand you being annoyed, but——'

'I'm not annoyed,' she denied, adding with emphasis, 'I am *furious*.'

'Oh, dear,' he said mildly. Then, with assumed gravity, 'Well, apart from the risk of us both catching chills, we can't have a fight standing dripping all over the hall carpet, so I suggest we get out of these wet things first.'

It was borne upon her that he'd said 'we'. But she could hardly expect him to stay wet and uncomfortable while she was warm and dry.

Torn between a desire to have it out with him and a dawning realisation that it might be wiser to send him packing with a flea in his ear, she hesitated.

The need to let off steam proved stronger than the voice of caution. Thrusting his jacket at him, she said, 'You know where the downstairs bathroom is, and there are plenty of towels in the airing cupboard.'

Her hair in dripping rat's-tails, the skirt of her dress clinging damply around her knees, she stalked up the stairs with as much dignity as she could muster, only too aware that he was standing there watching her.

If anything the storm had grown worse, the sheet lightning almost constant and dazzling as magnesium flares, while thunder cracked and rolled practically overhead.

The angels were certainly going to town.

And in a few minutes, Angie thought with grim humour, *this* Angel was about to let off her very own fireworks.

CHAPTER FIVE

THE delicious smell of percolating coffee greeted her as, dried and fully dressed, her hair bundled anyhow into a damp knot, Angie descended the stairs, ready for the fray.

Hearing the rhythmic whoosh of the tumble-drier, and recalling Adam's saturated shirt, she approached the kitchen cautiously.

His timing again annoyingly faultless, he was standing by the table, thoroughly at home, pouring coffee into two brown pottery mugs.

Prepared for the sight of his bare chest, she was totally *unprepared* to find him stark naked except for one of her peach towels knotted casually around his lean hips.

Swallowing, she looked anywhere but at him.

Well aware of her consternation, he handed her a mug of coffee, and, after surveying her blue, button-up-to-the-neck blouse and neat skirt with open derision, remarked, 'Though I'm not actually dressed, I'm really quite decent. There's no need for you to avert your eyes so modestly.'

That was all he knew!

Taking a gulp of the coffee and nearly scalding herself in the process, she girded her loins with anger and, golden eyes flashing, went verbally into battle.

'For being overbearing and arrogant, you take the biscuit!'

Raising a dark brow, he said mildly, 'Suppose, instead of reviling me, you tell me exactly what you're so annoyed about.'

'You know perfectly well what I'm annoyed about. Why did you have to involve Simon? Spring things on him the way you did?'

'I thought it best he should know the facts without delay. And he can't very well complain. It was *he* who suggested you should find yourself another husband.'

'It was unkind, to say the least,' she accused.

'Is there a kind way to let a man know he's finally lost a valuable property? And was *he* kind to you?'

'Two wrongs don't make a right.'

Undisturbed by this somewhat sanctimonious retort, Adam said, 'In my opinion he deserved all he got.'

'You're utterly despicable and...and *devious*.'

'Devious?' Head tilted back a little, he gave her a quizzical glance through long, thick lashes. 'I thought I was accused of being too straightforward?'

His lazy amusement made her angrier than ever. 'You led me to believe you were Adam Langford when really you were Adam Wingwood.'

'What difference does it make what I'm called?'

'All the difference in the world when you're *Sir Adam*! If I'd known I would never have——'

'Asked me to marry you?' His firm lips curved in a little smile. 'Why not?'

Her colour deepening still further, she snapped, 'It must be obvious why not.'

'Oh? Does being *Sir Adam*——' there was almost a sneer in his voice '—disqualify me from being a husband? Make me impossible to live with? Alter my looks or character? Turn me into a wife-beater?'

A flash of fork lightning made her flinch. 'If you'd told me, been honest instead of deliberately deceiving me...'

'I had no intention of deliberately deceiving you.'

'In that case why did you let me believe you were only a steward?'

Just for a moment he appeared discomfited, then he answered, 'Because in effect that's all I am. I told you the Hall with its inner park is entailed. I'm merely looking after it for my children.'

Dismissing that piece of reasoning as sophistry, she demanded, 'Have you considered you might, as a man with one annulled marriage, have problems in that direction?'

Eyes glinting, his slight Australian drawl in evidence, he said, 'I'd never heard that having an annulment made a man impotent.'

Angie gritted her teeth. 'I mean it might hamper you when you're ready to marry for keeps, marry someone of your own class.'

'I fail to see that it would make the slightest difference,' he disagreed flatly. Then after a moment, 'So now you've got all that off your chest, can we settle on a wedding date?'

She choked. 'No, we can't. If you were the last man on earth I wouldn't marry you! And for the life of me I fail to see why you're still prepared to go through with it.'

'Oh? Do you suppose that being *Sir Adam*——' again that scorn '—gives me less reason to want the island?'

'Oh . . .' she said, with a different inflexion. She'd forgotten about the island.

Coolly he continued, 'Don't you think, on reflection, that being a Wingwood provides a stronger, more logical reason to want it back? If Paula got her hands on the property it's possible I might lose it forever.'

Even through her anger she recognised the truth of that. If she let what had happened, or who he was, throw her, they might both end up losers.

She sighed.

Normally placid and sunny-natured, over the last few weeks her emotions had run high. She seemed to have been involved in more than her fair share of arguments and upsets, and was weary of them.

Reading her face aright, he said, 'So suppose we kiss and make friends?'

Padding up on bare feet, he was suddenly much too close.

Her heart starting to race, she took a hasty step backwards, then another. He was still advancing when she came up against the cupboards.

His hands one each side of her head, trapping her there without actually touching her, he gave a taunting little smile.

Throughout her tirade he had remained calm and tolerant, making no attempt to fight back. But he wasn't a man to let her get away with such behaviour scot-free, and this, she realised too late, was his revenge.

Turning her face away, she muttered frantically, 'I don't want to kiss you.'

'All right,' he agreed. Then magnanimously, 'To show there are no hard feelings, *I'll* kiss *you*.'

His lips brushed her cheek in a feather-light caress, then dropped to the corner of her mouth, where they lingered tantalisingly.

She could feel the heat of his body, smell his clean, sharp cologne, hear his quickened breathing. Or was it her own?

He began to draw away and she turned her head, only to discover the move was premature. She found herself looking straight into, and drowning in, those clear greeny-blue eyes, hypnotic and deep, fascinating as the sea.

'I love you in glasses,' he said in a low, sexy murmur. 'They make your eyes look enormous... But they do get in the way.' Before she could form any kind of protest, he'd taken them off and put them on top of the fridge.

When he bent again to touch his mouth to hers her eyes closed and her lips parted as though there was no help for it. He kissed her with a sweetness, an expertise, that set every nerve in her body tingling, and triggered off a response she could in no way hide.

Of their own accord, her hands came up to rest against his bare chest. Beneath her palms she could feel the warmth of his flesh, the fine sprinkling of crisp, dark hair, the strong beat of his heart.

His tongue-tip stroked slowly, erotically along her soft inner lip, that light touch making liquid fire run through her veins.

Desire flaring, she pressed herself against him in total abandon, longing to have his body touch hers, wanting him as she'd never wanted any man.

But instead of holding her closer, deepening the kiss, he drew away.

Opening dazed, bewildered eyes, she found he was watching her closely, his expression dissecting, calculating, disturbing in the extreme.

Blinking a little, she strove to pull herself together and hide the excitement still raging.

He smiled, as if he knew exactly what she was thinking and feeling and was pleased about it.

Red-hot desire turning to white-hot rage, she felt a primitive urge to wipe that ironic, self-satisfied smile from his lips with a well-aimed swipe.

'Better not,' he advised softly, as though she'd telexed her intention.

Bitterly she said, 'Don't tell me; let me guess... You'd hit me back.'

A hardness along his jawline, more than a hint of sensuality to his mouth, he replied calmly, 'That wouldn't be necessary. I could teach you a lesson without having to resort to violence.'

'You are the most——'

'That's enough, Angel.' He spoke with a quiet command that made the angry words die on her lips.

Then, gently rubbing her nose in it, 'I'm quite aware how disappointed you feel, but one of us had to keep control. After all,' he added reasonably, 'we're not even married yet. I doubt if you really want to wake up tomorrow morning and find me in your bed.'

Answering the dawning look of horror on her face, he said, 'No, I thought not. But if things hot up again, I must warn you that that's what will happen. I have no liking for the wham, bam, thank you, ma'am way of doing things. Given the right partner, I prefer to take my sex slow and easy, wring the last ounce of pleasure from it, so I——'

But Angie, scarlet-faced, and reduced to abject confusion by a combination of shame, anger, consternation and the erotic picture his words conjured up, had had enough. With perhaps the greatest effort of her life, she pulled herself together and broke in levelly, 'There's really no need to go on. I get the picture. And I can assure you that things won't be allowed to "hot up" again.'

Sighing, she added deliberately, 'I'm afraid I'm missing Simon,' and watched, with satisfaction, the impotent fury gather on Adam's face.

He turned away, showing her his striking, angular profile, and without another word began to take his clothes from the drier.

Her attempt to turn the tables had been even more successful than she'd hoped, though it was hard to say which had disturbed him most—the belief that she and Simon had been lovers, or the realisation that he could have served as a stand-in for her ex-fiancé.

He was a strange combination: arrogant yet unassuming, hard as granite, yet, she was sure, capable of great tenderness. He would make a wonderful, exciting

lover... She broke off the thought as if she were snapping
a dry twig.

If she was going to marry Adam, for both their sakes
she must learn to regard him not as a powerfully attractive male, but as a brother.

He had said, and she believed him, 'I won't do anything you don't want me to do'. So the onus had been
on her. She could hardly blame him for her lamentable
lack of self-control.

But after what had happened, before she married him
it might be as well to prove to them both that she could
remain immune to his potent sex appeal...

A crack of thunder which seemed to rattle the casements made her realise that the storm was still raging.
Lightning continued to illuminate the sky every few seconds and torrents of rain were being hurled against the
leaded panes.

His shirt and trousers over his arm, Adam was heading
for the bathroom when, taking the plunge, she asked
hurriedly, 'Are you going to put your clothes back on?'

Raising a mocking brow, he remarked, 'You sound
disappointed.'

Gesturing at the streaming windows, she explained a
shade breathlessly, 'What I mean is, it's still pouring
down.'

He feigned surprise. 'So it is!'

Ignoring his levity, she continued desperately, 'You'll
be wet through again before you get home.'

'Well, I suppose I could go naked,' he said, his voice
thoughtful. 'But although the track's quiet, I can't lose
sight of the fact that it's still public. I don't want to get
locked up...'

With a quizzical grin, he suggested, 'Or would you
feel safer if I was?'

'Not at all.' She reacted to his mockery with a coolness
she was far from feeling. 'In fact I was going to suggest

you stay here. I always keep the bed in the guest-room made up, so it's no trouble. If you need some pyjamas there's a new pair in——'

'I don't.'

She swallowed, and, beginning to regret her rashness, said hastily, 'But you haven't a toothbrush or anything... Thinking about it, it was a silly thing to suggest. You'll be far more comfortable at home and...' Realising he was purposely letting her run on, she stopped abruptly.

Lazily he murmured, 'I think it's an excellent idea. I'm more than happy to accept your kind hospitality.' Eyes glinting, he added coaxingly, 'So if you'd care to show me my room?'

Whether by accident or design, he wasn't making it easy for her.

Standing stock-still, she informed him, 'It's the second door on the left.'

'Thank you.' Smiling at her, he wheedled plaintively, 'I always have a hot milky drink in bed. It helps me sleep.'

He *looked* the kind of man who couldn't go to bed without a hot milky drink, she thought ironically. And certain now that his blandishments were by *design*, she bit back an acid retort in which the word 'wimp' featured strongly, and said with saccharine sweetness, 'Please feel free to take one up with you.'

'Shall I bring *you* one?' he suggested hopefully. 'I like having someone to share things with.'

Trying to remain stoical in the face of such devilment, she answered, 'No, thank you,' adding quite untruthfully, 'I *hate* milky drinks.' Then, feeling the urge to retaliate, 'But if you want someone to share it with you, Tosca enjoys a saucer of sweet cocoa.'

As she fled, Angie thought she heard his soft laugh.

Having hastily cleaned her teeth and prepared for bed, she lay awake in a room lit periodically by lightning and listened tensely for his step on the stairs.

Knowing comparatively little about him, had she been a fool? Almost immediately she dismissed the doubt. In spite of his teasing, she trusted him.

But what if he tried her door and, finding it unlocked, construed that as an invitation?

No, he wouldn't do any such thing, she told herself stoutly. Earlier, in the kitchen, he'd been the one to call a halt, to point out that she wouldn't want to wake and find him in her bed.

Perhaps the noise of the storm masked the creak of the stairs, because eventually she relaxed and fell asleep without having heard him come up.

A tapping at her door awoke her and she opened her eyes to a room full of sunlight. At the same instant, recollection of what had taken place the previous night, and realisation of just *who* was waiting outside, brought her bolt upright, chills running through her.

'Yes?' It came out in the nature of a half-strangled squeak.

But as if that was invitation enough, he walked in, carrying a tray of tea and wearing an old towelling bathrobe that had once belonged to Ben. On him it was both too short and too tight and, though it was belted, the width of his chest and shoulders threatened to make it pull apart any second.

Seeing her gazing at it, he remarked cheerfully, 'I thought it was a shade more respectable than a towel.'

That was a matter of opinion!

'What's wrong with your clothes?' she demanded, trying to hide how rattled she was.

'Not a thing,' he replied innocently. 'But I always have a cup of tea before I shower and dress. Besides, *you're* still in your nightie——' a smile tugging at his lips, he eyed the sprigged muslin with its high round neckline '—so it makes it more cosy.'

'Cosy' was the last thing she wanted it to be.

Clear eyes gleaming with health and vitality, hair rumpled, a dark stubble adorning his chin, he was dangerously, devastatingly sexy and attractive.

Having handed her a cup, he sat down companionably on the edge of the bed, raising the hair on the back of her neck and making a fine dew of perspiration break out all over her body.

'What's the matter, Angel?' he asked, obviously enjoying her discomfort.

'Nothing's the matter,' she denied hoarsely. 'It's just that I'm not used to having tea in bed.'

'Oh?' Then with a sudden sharpness to his tone, 'Didn't Perry ever bring you morning tea and biscuits?'

About to reply, Certainly not, she pulled herself up and answered obliquely, 'Simon doesn't drink tea. He's very health conscious. He considers caffeine, and biscuits, bad for him.'

The contemptuous twist to Adam's lips made it quite clear what he was thinking.

'Speaking of biscuits——' reaching for the solitary digestive, he broke it in two '—we'll share.'

'You told me you *liked* sharing, but isn't one between us rather scrimping?'

'This is all there is left.'

Blinking in the sun, she watched him dunk his half, a habit Simon deplored, and asked, 'What happened to the rest?'

'Tosca did. I put them down too close to the edge of the table.'

His sudden grin made him damn nigh irresistible.

She swallowed hard. 'That was unwise.'

'Ah, well, I can be as foolish as the next man.' Taking her empty cup and putting it on the tray, he leaned towards her and, his eyes darkening to sea-jade, said softly, 'Just at the moment I have a foolish fancy to run my fingers through your hair.'

Her heart began to do back somersaults, and warmth filled her. With only a look, a few words, he had the power to turn her into a different person, someone who had discovered needs and fierce feelings she hadn't known existed.

His voice becoming deeper, warmer, seductive as black velvet, he went on, 'A lot of women couldn't stand so much light first thing in the morning, but it shows your skin is flawless, and turns your hair into strands of silk tangled with sunshine... I want to play with it, spread it across the pillow, bury my face in it... I want to hold your head between my hands and kiss you...'

Trying to sound calm, but only succeeding in sounding breathless and agitated, she objected, 'If you kiss me with that stubble I'm going to look as if my face has been sandpapered.'

He smiled wickedly. 'In that case I'll have to kiss you some place it doesn't show.'

She sat as though spellbound while he began to undo the tiny covered buttons on the yoke of her nightdress. With only two to go, a loud banging on the front door accompanied by a fusillade of barks broke the spell.

Muttering something that could have been a curse, Adam rose to his feet, then, having glanced out of the window, said swiftly, 'I'll go; you're not dressed.'

Neither was he.

With a sudden horrified comprehension of what it would look like if a half-naked man answered her door at this time of the morning, she fastened the buttons, pulled on her robe, and flew downstairs after him.

She was five seconds too late. By the time she'd reached the bottom, Adam had thrown the door wide and was saying with what sounded suspiciously like complacency, 'I'm afraid we were still upstairs, but do come in. I'll go and tell Angel you're here——'

'Don't bother!'

Crossing the hall at a trot, Angie caught just a glimpse of Simon's furious face before he turned and rushed down the path.

When she would have followed, Adam took hold of her wrist in a light yet steely grip, 'Let him go, Angel.'

'But he thinks——'

'Of course he does.' Adam's voice held satisfaction.

With a sudden jerk that took him by surprise, she pulled free and ran in bare feet after Simon, calling his name.

No matter what, she couldn't let him go like this; she *had* to explain. Breathless, she caught up with him at the gate. 'Wait, please wait...'

He turned and looked at her, taking in her night attire and her uncombed hair with burning eyes.

Even without her glasses, she saw the red tide wash into his face. Practically gibbering with rage, he cried, 'How *could* you act like this? We were engaged for months and all you did was put me off, saying we should wait until we were married. You've scarcely known him a week, yet you couldn't wait to jump into bed with *him*.'

'I haven't been to bed with him! It isn't how it looks. You see, when he brought me home last night it——'

Gazing at the white hatchback parked behind Angie's old Ford, Simon broke in, 'I wondered whose car that was... So why is it still in your drive? And what the devil is he doing in your house with only a bathrobe on?'

Flushing a little, she said, 'I asked him stay. He spent the night in the guest room.'

'Why? His own place is only a hundred yards away.'

'Well, it was pouring with rain and——'

'And you thought he might dissolve! You must take me for an utter fool,' Simon snarled.

'I know it must sound pretty unconvincing,' she admitted. 'All the same, it *is* the truth. I wasn't in bed with him and I haven't slept with him.'

'Don't try to deny that he was in your room. As soon as he answered the door I realised it must have been *him* I caught sight of through the bedroom window.'

'Yes, he was in my room, but it was quite innocent.' Quite innocent? her conscience queried scornfully. Slapping it down, she rushed on, 'He'd just brought me a cup of tea.'

'A likely story.'

'It happens to be true. In any case, it's no longer your concern. You told me to find someone else.'

Looking sullen, Simon protested, 'You must know I didn't mean it. I only wanted to bring you to your senses.'

'Well, you succeeded. You made me realise our engagement had been a mistake from start to finish. We aren't suited, and we could never have made each other happy.'

His face a mottled plum colour, Simon accused, 'You didn't think that until you saw a chance of becoming Lady Wingwood . . .'

'I'm afraid you're wrong there, Perry,' Adam, who had sauntered up unheard and unobserved, corrected calmly.

Despite being barefoot, he was as tall as Simon, and his splendid physique and mature width of shoulder made the other man look almost weedy.

With quiet emphasis he went on, 'When I asked Angel to marry me, she accepted, thinking I was plain Adam Langford. She hadn't the faintest idea I belonged to the

Wingwood family until Mrs Hunter-Gore gave the game away.'

For a moment Simon looked disconcerted, then, light suddenly dawning, he said nastily, 'In that case, shall I tell you *why* she accepted? *Why* she was ready to snap your hand off?'

'She accepted for the same reason that I proposed. The attraction was strong and mutual. We both knew instantly that we were right for one another.'

Stepping closer, Adam clapped a hand on Simon's padded shoulder, making him jump, and added with a spurious air of friendliness that barely disguised the silky menace, 'I wouldn't like it if anyone should happen to think differently... So I'm sure I can rely on you not to encourage any silly rumours.'

The instant Adam lifted his hand, Simon hurriedly put the gate between them. A moment later he dived into his car and took off down the rutted track with none of his usual care for the Mercedes's suspension.

Adam chuckled.

Turning, Angie rushed back into the house, Adam at her heels, and stormed through to the kitchen. Rescuing her glasses from the top of the fridge, where he'd placed them the night before, she thrust them on to her nose with an unsteady hand.

Then, feeling more like herself, she cried, 'How *could* you?'

He gave her a pseudo-innocent look. 'Now what am I being accused of?'

'You threatened him!'

'I don't recall doing that.'

'Or as good as... And then you laughed!'

'Didn't you think it was funny, the way he ran like a frightened rabbit?'

'No, I didn't.'

Truth to tell, she'd been trying to repress a smile when Adam's open laughter had rubbed her the wrong way. Guilt brought renewed irritation. 'There was no need to treat him so abominably, *intimidate* him.'

'Do you want him to start telling the world our business?'

'No, but I...' When she faltered to a halt, he raised a questioning brow.

Looking into his dark, steely face, she let that go and went in from another angle. 'You knew perfectly well who was at the door and you answered on purpose. You wanted to make him think we'd been in bed together... Don't try to deny it.'

'I wasn't going to,' Adam said calmly.

Often he was subtle, complex and, when he wanted to be, hard to read, but now something about his smug expression carried her conjecture a stage further. 'You *expected* him to come——'

'Didn't you?'

She'd had so many other things on her mind that it had never occurred to her.

Ignoring the interruption, she ploughed on, 'That's why you stayed the night. You didn't *want* to go home.'

'I was under the impression *you* didn't want me to.'

Pink-cheeked, she said, 'I was just concerned that you shouldn't get wet again.'

Softly he pointed out, 'You *could* have loaned me a mac or an umbrella.'

That hadn't occurred to her either.

Her desire to prove to them both that she could remain immune to his sexual charisma had obsessed her, blocking the logical workings of her mind. But he must have thought... She felt her face grow even hotter. No wonder he'd teased her.

Apparently taking pity on her, he briskly changed the subject. 'How about something to eat?'

'I . . . I'd better put some clothes on first.'

'Why don't you shower and dress while I cook? I'm a dab hand at bacon and eggs.'

She glanced at his long, muscular legs and the barely adequate bathrobe, then looked hurriedly away.

His face deadpan, he offered, 'If it disturbs you, I'll get dressed too.'

'It doesn't make any difference to me,' she lied hardily.

He saluted her spirit, then said in a businesslike tone, 'In that case, off you go. We've a busy day ahead, all the wedding arrangements to be made, so over breakfast we ought to decide on a suitable date . . . Don't you agree?'

Remembering the little scene in her bedroom, the way she felt whenever he touched her, she hesitated.

Suppose she couldn't keep their relationship on a business footing? He'd made no secret of the fact that he wouldn't find it easy to live like a monk for a year. *And she wanted him.* But whereas most men could have a sexual relationship without their emotions being involved, a lot of women couldn't.

And she was one.

Finally she faced it. What if this heady attraction wasn't just physical. If she went through with the marriage and found herself in love with him, she could end up losing a lot more than Clouds . . .

But she was being an absolute idiot, she scolded herself, looking for complications that didn't exist. What she felt for Adam was plain old-fashioned lust, and that was problem enough.

However, lust *could*, and *should*, be kept under control. Though she hadn't been too successful so far, a demon of doubt taunted her.

'Well, Angel?' There was the slightest touch of impatience in his voice.

Helplessly, she agreed, 'I . . . I suppose so.'

His eyes registering obvious displeasure, he said coldly, 'I can stand you furious, I can stand you resentful, but I can't stand you defeated and submissive. If, despite everything, Simon means that much to you, go after him and tell him so, and we'll call our agreement off.'

She could only be pleased that he hadn't guessed the real reason for her hesitation.

Squaring her shoulders, she said with a touch of hauteur, 'I don't want to call it off. And you're quite right, we should decide on a suitable date without delay.'

When she got down again, he too was showered and dressed, and the appetising smell of bacon and eggs and toast filled the cheerful kitchen.

They ate in silence, then, Angie having poured the coffee, Adam said abruptly, 'Suppose we say the seventeenth, by special licence? I'll see Hallfield's vicar this morning.'

'Oh, but I thought... I mean, we want to keep everything low-key. Wouldn't it be better to get married at the register office?'

'I'm not in favour of a register office.' His tone was uncompromising. 'And why should we keep things low-key? As it's the first time for both of us, I suggest we have all the trimmings.'

'But surely it isn't necessary, or even sensible, to spend so much money?'

Quietly adamant, he said, 'I know this marriage isn't for what you might describe as the "usual" reasons, but I refuse to have it look like some cheap, hole-and-corner affair. Or as if we've got something to be ashamed of.'

Finally Angie admitted the truth. 'Well, I...I wouldn't be *comfortable*. I mean, I don't really think it's right to make vows I've no intention of keeping. And as it's only a marriage of convenience ...'

Adam's face hardened perceptibly. 'Do you want the whole world to know that?'

'Well, no, but...'

'No buts.' An edge to his voice, he added, 'Even if you consider you can't wear white, I'd like a traditional wedding. A bride I can be proud of. And the *appearance* at least of a happy couple who mean to make it last.'

Trying not to feel piqued by his remark about wearing white—after all, it was her own fault he thought as he did—she put her scruples aside, not without some feeling of transgression, and agreed, 'Very well.'

If that was what he wanted, then she owed it to him to do the best she could. And with her usual good sense she decided that even if she felt like an actress playing a role she wasn't totally happy with she might as well try, for both their sakes, to enjoy it.

Once the wedding arrangements had been made she saw comparatively little of him, and each time they met he treated her with a cool aloofness that made her wonder if he was regretting their bargain.

On one occasion only did he seem more like himself. He'd popped in that evening to settle a minor detail when the conversation somehow got round to passport photographs. Having admitted how bad his was, he teased her into digging hers out of the bureau drawer to show him.

'Well, I've seen worse,' he said, surveying it critically. 'It doesn't flatter you, but at least you look relatively normal, whereas I bear a striking resemblance to Mephistopheles.'

'How apt,' she murmured, and received a menacing look for her impudence.

The following morning he appeared at her door to say he was going up to London for the weekend.

'Business or pleasure?' She tried to keep her voice light.

'Possibly both,' he answered drily. 'Though I expect to be back by Monday.'

'Are you planning to see Paula?'

Damn! She hadn't meant to ask that. If he was seeing Paula, she didn't want to know.

Narrowed eyes on her face, he queried, 'Would you mind if I was?'

She minded more than she cared to admit, even to herself. 'It isn't really any of my business,' she answered stiffly.

On what seemed to be an afterthought, he asked, 'You will be all right up here on your own?'

'Of course.' Frostily she added, 'I was on my own before you came.'

But it was no longer the same, she admitted, when he'd driven off.

She'd got used to the open windows and smoke rising from the chimneys of the cottage next door, used to the sight of Adam, the faint sound of his radio, the knowledge that he was close at hand.

Now, without him, she was not just alone, but *lonely*. While he would almost certainly be enjoying Paula's company, having a final fling.

At least she *hoped* it was final, Angie thought painfully.

He'd told her, 'As a married man—albeit in name only—I won't be doing any roaming'. She could only pray he'd meant it.

Though she had no real claim on his fidelity, she knew her happiness, her peace of mind for the next year, would depend on it.

CHAPTER SIX

ANGIE and Adam were married the following Thursday in the old grey village church, with only a few friends present.

The bride wore a simple but lovely ankle-length gown in ivory satin and, having removed her glasses for the occasion, and left her hair loose, a coronet of fresh flowers to hold in place a short veil.

Sara, a friend from her schooldays, had chosen a bridesmaid's dress of deep apricot, which suited her glossy dark hair. Both of them carried sprays of creamy rosebuds and pale, scented freesias.

Andrew Bolton, Sara's father and an old friend of Ben's, gave the bride away, while his son, Timothy, made a quiet but conscientious best man.

After the register was signed, in Angie's case a trifle blearily, and they'd posed in the fitful morning sunshine for some photographs, Adam took the wedding party and the half a dozen guests for an early lunch at the best hotel in Darfield.

It was a small but friendly group, and though they'd each and every one been surprised by the sudden switch in wedding plans—not to mention bridegrooms—all appeared delighted, especially Sara, who, she now admitted, had never liked Simon, considering him both bossy and querulous.

As soon as the single-tier cake was cut, and the various toasts made, Adam—looking as tall, dark and devastatingly handsome as any bride could have wished—took Angie's hand and pulled her to her feet.

Putting a proprietorial arm around her, he said to the assembled company, 'Please feel free to stay and enjoy yourselves for as long as you wish, but it's time we went up to get changed.'

'Get changed? What on earth did you tell them that for?' Angie whispered as, clutching her bouquet, she was hurried across the red-carpeted functions room and into the lift.

Between thick lashes his dark greeny-blue eyes glinted. 'Did you want them to think I was taking you upstairs because I couldn't wait to make mad, passionate love to you?'

Apart from a chaste kiss after the ceremony, when he'd replaced her engagement ring on top of her plain gold wedding-band, this was the first time he'd made the slightest attempt to provoke or unsettle her.

But dynamite was still dynamite, even if she'd made the mistake of starting to take it for granted.

Holding tightly to her composure, she asked, 'Why *are* you taking me upstairs?'

'Because the room I hired for you to change in happens to be on the top floor.'

Bewildered, she protested, 'I haven't brought anything to change *into*.'

'I've had your things sent up.'

'Sent up...? But why do I need to change here?'

'If you go home to do it, we'll miss our plane.'

'Plane?' She'd begun to sound like a parrot, she thought crossly. 'What are you talking about?'

'I'm talking about our honeymoon.' Casually he went on, 'I thought we should have one for the look of the thing.'

'You never said anything about a honeymoon.' She was instantly tense, her golden-brown eyes wary.

'I decided to keep it for a surprise.'

'But I can't go on honeymoon.' She had thought herself safeguarded and there was panic in her voice when, the lift doors having slid open, he began to urge her across the corridor and into a small sitting-room. As though it clinched matters, she added, 'Simon and I weren't having a honeymoon.'

'Oh? Whose decision was that? Yours?'

It had been Simon's. And, though seeing the sense of it, she'd felt more than a little disappointed, being a romantic at heart. Now, a shade defensively, she said, 'Simon himself said I couldn't very well leave the animals.'

'You've married *me*, not Simon,' Adam pointed out, a trifle curtly.

'It's just not possible.' She dug her toes in.

'It's perfectly possible,' he told her levelly. 'Everything's been taken care of.'

'How do you mean?'

'Start to get changed and I'll tell you.'

The cream and blue suit which she had originally intended to get married in was hanging on a rail, its matching blouse and accessories close at hand.

'Let me help you.' Adam came up behind her and carefully lifted the coronet from silky hair the pale colour of ripe corn.

Then, with an amazingly sensitive touch for such strong, muscular hands, he began to unfasten the tiny hooks and eyes down the back of her dress.

Though he barely brushed her skin she felt her breath quicken and her pulses start to race, as they'd done earlier in church when his lips had merely touched her cheek.

As soon as the hooks were all undone he moved to the window, and, his dark, well-shaped head turned, stood looking across the hotel gardens, while she hastily stepped out of the dress and long slip.

'How do you mean, "taken care of"?' Resolutely she went back to the issue in hand.

She was standing in her ivory lace-trimmed bra and briefs and suspender belt when he swung round to answer.

Judging by the gleam in his eyes, Adam approved unreservedly of the delicate, semi-transparent fabric.

Snatching up the blouse, she held it to her chest, afraid he would see what effect his merely *looking* at her had.

'There's no need to be *quite* so modest,' he said with derision. 'It's nothing I haven't seen before.'

Gritting her teeth, she began to dress, while sticking determinedly to her guns. 'Would you mind telling me what you mean by "taken care of"? Tosca——'

'Tosca will be fine. As you well know, she's perfectly happy at Fife Cottage...'

That was the truth. During the last week or so the bull-terrier had spent almost as much time with Adam as she had at home.

'And because I won't actually be living there when we get back I've engaged a housekeeper.'

'A housekeeper? Angie was startled.

'A nice, respectable widow named Gladys Pimm, who used to work at the Hall when I was a boy. I offered her the job last week and she moved in and was introduced to Tosca first thing this morning.'

Knowing she was fighting a losing battle, Angie protested, 'But what about Barnaby and Nicholas?'

'Mrs Pimm was born and bred on a farm.' Watching his wife pull on gossamer silk stockings and fasten her suspenders, Adam sounded somewhat *distrait*.

Angie played her trump card. 'But surely we can't *afford* to go on honeymoon?'

Not a whit disturbed, he disagreed. 'Oh, I think we can... So if that's answered all your doubts...?'

'I suppose so,' she said grudgingly.

It had answered all she dared actually *mention*, but her biggest doubt was whether she could cope with a honeymoon.

Managing an air of insouciance, she asked, 'Where are we going?'

'Lake Como,' he answered. 'Surrounded by mountains, it's beautiful and romantic, with cypress trees like dark green fingers against a blue, blue sky, and little lake steamers.' His voice deepening, he added, 'An ideal spot for a honeymoon.'

'You sound as if you know it well,' she remarked in a somewhat strangled voice.

'I do. Though most of my visits were made when I was still a child. Have you ever been to Italy?'

She recovered herself. 'Only once. Ben took me to Rome when I was just sixteen.'

'Did you like it?'

'Oh, yes.' The enthusiasm was unforced. 'I adored the sunshine, the colour, the people, the atmosphere...' Then with a grin, 'And especially the food. All that lovely pasta and——'

'You're a gannet,' Adam said severely, but his eyes were amused. 'I can see you coming back weighing all of eight stone.'

When he'd removed the white carnation from the lapel of his well-cut grey suit, he produced her glasses from his pocket and, having set them with precision on her nose, queried, 'Nearly ready? It's high time we were off.'

'Oh, but what about my things?' She glanced at her wedding finery.

'The hotel have agreed to store them.'

Another thought struck her. 'I've no clothes to take with me, nothing packed...'

'It's all been organised. I gave Mrs Pimm a key to Clouds and as soon as your hired car had left for church she slipped in and put everything she thought you'd need

into a case. It was delivered here and stowed in the boot
of my car while we were having lunch.'

'But I haven't...' She stopped short. 'I suppose *you've*
got my passport.'

Adam appeared undaunted by the note of accusation
her question contained. 'It's in my pocket,' he admitted
complacently. 'I was forced to appropriate it when your
back was turned.'

She tried one last shot. 'But if it's still in my maiden
name...'

Patiently he said, 'The vicar assures me that, with our
marriage certificate to prove your change of name and
status, we should have no problems. Ready now?'

Conceding defeat, she nodded.

'Don't forget this.' He picked up her fragile bouquet
with that delicate sureness of touch.

Taking it from him, she thought that Simon, for all
his slender hands and tapering fingers, would have
mangled it.

Their small party was assembled on the steps of the
hotel to send them off in a shower of rice and confetti.
Just before she climbed into the car, Angie turned to
wave and throw her bouquet.

Timothy's girlfriend caught it and, smiling and
blushing, leaned against him with an eloquent glance.

'We haven't a lot of time,' Adam remarked, as he slid
behind the wheel, 'but, all being well, we shouldn't miss
our plane.'

It was a smooth flight lasting less than three hours, and
after an early dinner on board the aircraft they arrived
at Milan's Malpensa airport in the sun and warmth of
a lovely summer evening.

A hired car was waiting, and Adam dealt with the
formalities in what sounded to Angie's untutored ear to
be fluent Italian.

When he had stowed their luggage in the boot of the fawn Fiat he took off his jacket and got in beside her. The powerful width of his shoulders, the effect of so much disturbing masculinity in the confines of the small car, threatened to overwhelm her.

Glancing at that strong face—the bony nose and thrusting jaw, the austere mouth with its hint of sensuality, the sweep of long, curly lashes against hard cheekbones as he looked down—she felt her whole body flush with heat.

Her throat dry, she remarked a shade wildly, 'I don't even know where we're heading, except that it's on Lake Como.'

Tossing his jacket over to the back seat, he rolled his white silk shirt-sleeves up tanned, muscular arms lightly sprinkled with dark hair, before answering, 'We're going to the Villa dei Fiori at Menezzo.'

There was a peculiar inflexion in his voice that made her hazard, 'You've been there before?'

'Many times.'

'Is it a big place?'

'No, not very.'

'How long will it take us?'

'About an hour and a half.'

Seeing he was abstracted, disinclined to talk, Angie sat back to enjoy the drive, which after a while took them through some richly wooded hills and spectacular scenery, with enticing glimpses of blue water through the dark green pines.

Finally the road wound down into Menezzo, which climbed like terraced grape-vines from the edge of the lake. Over the far mountains a magnificent sunset hovered, bathing the small, picturesque town in rose and gold.

'It used to be a fishing village,' Adam broke the silence, 'but now tourism has taken over.'

They drove through narrow streets full of character and colour until, on the outskirts of the village, they reached a pair of tall black wrought-iron gates standing invitingly open. On either side was a stone nymph wearing a seraphic expression and a garland of flowers.

Having followed a pale gravel drive curling through a green and luxuriant garden, they drew up in front of a whitewashed villa.

Its walls were clothed in trailing wistaria and flowering creeper, which even encroached on its pink pantiles. Masses of brilliant geraniums spilt from window-boxes, while scented roses and honeysuckle clambered over arches and balconies.

'Villa dei Fiori.' Adam verified that they had reached their destination. 'What do you think of it?'

Sucking breath into suddenly constricted lungs, she protested weakly, 'This isn't a hotel.'

He raised a dark brow. 'Did I ever say it was?'

'Well, no... But I presumed...'

Softly, with a hint of silky menace, he said, 'Don't you know it's dangerous to presume anything, Angel?'

Despite the heat, a chill ran through her, raising the fine hairs on the back of her neck and making her shiver. Fighting down a swift, cowardly apprehension, she told herself she was being ridiculous. He was just teasing her.

Or was he?

As he helped her from the car she tried to dispel the unnerving doubt. She *did* trust him; she'd trusted him from the start.

But had she been a fool?

All through the ages women had trusted con men, philanderers, libertines, and worse...

Adam took her elbow in a light yet implacable grip and led her round the side of the building to an arched door with a long, deep-silled window on either side.

'Don't look so worried,' he said mockingly. 'Just because this is a private house rather than a hotel, it doesn't mean I'm planning rape or murder.'

'What *are* you planning?' She tried to keep her voice cool, uncaring even, but despite all her efforts it sounded uncertain, and her golden eyes looked scared.

For a moment Adam found himself almost deflected from his purpose. Though strong and capable in some ways, she was terribly vulnerable in others.

'Well?' she demanded, recovering her spirit.

'Nothing you won't like,' he answered obliquely, and opened the door with a large key he had retrieved from a pot of scarlet fuchsia on the windowsill.

The villa was open-plan, giving an immediate impression of being spacious and airy, with long windows, white archways, cool terrazzo tiling and masses of green plants.

Ushering her into the entrance hall, where a horseshoe staircase with wrought-iron banisters curved up to the next floor, he suggested, 'Why don't you have a look around while I bring in our cases and garage the car?'

His avuncular tone made her earlier panic seem ridiculous. If she hadn't been expecting a *hotel*, if she hadn't let herself be rattled by his remark about it being dangerous to *presume* anything, she would have had no cause to doubt him.

It was high time she stopped behaving like a fool, Angie told herself sternly, as she set out to explore.

Having ascended the elegant stairway, she found three good-sized bedrooms, handsomely furnished, each with a balcony and an *en-suite* bathroom.

The master bedroom, which overlooked the lake, had a luxurious canopied bed, the fine sheets turned down as though ready for instant occupation.

Downstairs there was a well-appointed kitchen, a pleasant dining area, and a most attractive sitting-room.

Outside the sitting-room a paved terrace looked across the blue water to the wooded hills opposite.

Taking off her jacket, she draped it over a chair and, having opened the French windows wide, went out to lean her elbows on the stone balustrade.

Scattered around were a couple of sun-loungers, a swing seat with a canopy, and a round table and chair set beneath a fringed umbrella.

To the left, steps led down to a small private beach, with a wooden raft moored about thirty yards from the shore.

Flowers were everywhere—in tubs and pots and hanging baskets, and growing in cracks and crevices along the stonework. They took on an almost luminous quality in the gathering dusk.

When Adam suddenly appeared by her side Angie nearly jumped out of her skin. She'd forgotten he moved lithely, silently, like a hunter.

'I didn't hear you coming.' All at once she was breathless.

He'd changed from his formal suit into an open-necked sports shirt and slim-fitting trousers, garments that unobtrusively showed off lean hips, wide shoulders and the strong column of his throat. He was carrying a bottle of iced champagne and two glasses.

Using the balustrade as a table, he eased the cork out with a satisfying pop and poured the smoking wine.

Accepting a glass, she watched the bubbles rising like tiny golden balls, while he watched her.

'Hungry?' he queried.

Though she'd had little to eat either at lunchtime or on the plane, the excitement of what seemed a very long day had taken away her usually excellent appetite. She shook her head. 'No, not really.'

Standing together, they sipped champagne as a myriad lights began to appear around the edges of the lake, pinpoints of brightness that twinkled like diamonds in the warm scented air.

To add the finishing touch, an ethereal moon rose above the dark treetops, washing the night in silver.

It was much too romantic.

Feeling the need to establish some kind of mundane normality, to lay the basis for their relationship over the next year, she asked as prosaically as possible, 'Who got everything ready for us and left the key?'

'Signora Ponti, who lives in the village and takes care of the place.'

'Is this where you used to come as a child?'

'Yes. It was owned by my mother's cousin, who was married to an Italian diplomat. What do you think of it as a place to honeymoon...?' he added lazily, dropping a light arm around her shoulders.

Very aware of his touch, she stood stock-still, knowing it would have been *idyllic* if only this had been a proper honeymoon... If only he'd loved her...

But that was an idiotic thought. Their marriage was simply a business arrangement.

All the same, she couldn't help feeling a strange twist of sadness that so much romance and magic was being wasted.

'Do you like it?' He stooped to murmur the question in her ear, and his breath stirred a stray tendril of hair.

After a pause to get her voice under control, she admitted slowly, 'It's absolutely beautiful.'

'So are you.'

His unexpected response threw her into total confusion. She took an unwary gulp of the champagne and coughed.

'Knowing I consider you beautiful seems to make you nervous,' he remarked, as he released her to refill their glasses.

Swallowing hard, she tried for flippancy. 'It only makes me believe your eyesight's bad.'

In the moonlight he studied her with a nerve-racking intentness. 'I don't mean a classical—or even a conventional—type of beauty. But there's a radiance in your face, warmth and passion in the curve of your mouth, dreams and enchantment in your eyes.'

His words, full of wicked charm, tied her stomach in knots. Taking another drink, she said jerkily, 'I still think you need spectacles.'

'Speaking of spectacles...' Reaching out, he lifted hers from her nose and slipped them into his shirt pocket.

'Why did you do that?' Her normally low-pitched, slightly husky voice sounded high and reedy.

'Because they get in the way if I kiss you.'

Falling back a panicky step, she blurted, 'But you're not going to kiss me.'

'I shouldn't bet on that if I were you.'

She gave him an apprehensive glance. 'But you promised you wouldn't.'

'As I told you on a previous occasion, I only promised I wouldn't do anything you didn't want me to do.'

'Well, I don't want you to kiss me.'

'Are you quite sure about that?' His voice was soft and deep.

'Quite sure. A kiss can lead to...' She faltered, then finished off defiantly, 'All sorts of things.'

'Just what I thought,' he agreed with satisfaction, as he refilled their glasses once more. 'That was one of the reasons I wanted to kiss you. Champagne, moonlight and romance should provide all the right ingredients for...' He paused deliberately.

'F-for what?' Without thinking, she downed some more of the sparkling wine, though already she felt slightly giddy.

He bent his dark head and, his lips brushing her ear, whispered, 'For the seduction I'm planning.'

She jerked away. 'I don't find that remotely funny.'

'It wasn't meant to be funny... After all, there can't be many bridegrooms who have to seduce their own bride.'

Trying to believe he was baiting her, she gave what should have been a light laugh, but didn't quite come off. 'You're not serious, of course...'

'Oh, but I am.'

This time there was no doubting him, and the wine in her glass shivered as her hand became unsteady.

'If you *are* serious why are you telling me this? I mean...'

'You mean it would have been easier to have gone ahead and taken you by surprise, rather than warning you?'

Her long, gold-tipped lashes flickered.

Blandly he continued, 'I'm sure you're right. But I decided it would be best to lay my cards on the table. I know you would prefer me to override your doubts and just take you, so tomorrow morning you can pretend to me and yourself that you weren't really willing. But in that I refuse to indulge you. We must be equal, consenting partners.'

His voice low and seductive, he added, 'All you need to do is come from behind those barricades you've thrown up. Admit you want me.'

Trying to sound confident, she assured him, 'I won't do that.' The words were a little slurred.

'Perhaps I could persuade you.' He lifted her hand to his lips and ran his tongue-tip over her finger-ends.

She gasped at the sensual caress, then shook her head, making it spin.

With deliberation he took her glass, which she'd been clutching like the proverbial straw, and placed it alongside his on the balustrade. 'Shall I put it to the test?'

'No! I don't want you to touch me.' Confidence forgotten, her voice cracked in panic, and a faint dew of perspiration sprang out on her temples. 'I'm going up to my room.'

'In that case, I'll kiss you goodnight.' He used the hand he was still imprisoning to draw her to him, before touching his lips lightly to her temple.

She was breathing a sigh of relief when he kissed her cheek and jaw and, nuzzling aside her silken fall of pale hair, let his mouth travel down the side of her neck, delicately sucking and nibbling.

A shock of pure pleasure jolted her. *Run*, her brain screamed, but her legs refused to obey the command, and she stood as still as one of the marble nymphs that watched over the gate.

'Decided to stay and fight?' She heard the smile in his voice, before his mouth resumed its torment.

Struggling to stay in control, she managed, 'I warn you, I'm not——'

'Easy to seduce? I'm sure you're not. But if Simon can do it, I consider it a challenge to my manhood.'

Trying to ignore the heated excitement, the fierce craving he was arousing in her, in a stifled whisper she objected, 'We agreed it was to be a marriage of convenience.'

'It will be a great deal more convenient for both of us if we make it a real marriage. A year is a long time. And what about you?'

'What about me?'

'A year's a long time for *you*.'

She felt his warm breath against her ear before his tongue-tip made an erotic exploration of the shell-like scroll-work.

'The night we got engaged and things hotted up, you admitted you were frustrated.'

'I did no such thing,' she gasped.

'Well, you certainly *acted* as if you were.'

Unable to deny the charge, she caught her lower lip between her teeth and stayed silent.

Drawing away a little to watch her perturbation, Adam went on ironically, 'It occurred to me that, though Perry's always struck me as a bit of a cold fish, perhaps he was Superman when he went into action——'

'Will you be good enough to leave Simon out of it?' she cried, taking refuge in anger.

'I'll be more than happy to. If we make ours a real marriage, there's no——'

'But it wouldn't *be* a real marriage,' she burst out fiercely. 'It would just be *sex* ...'

'What's wrong with sex, providing it's a good and joyful experience for both partners?'

'Nothing...' she conceded. Then with desperation, 'But as we don't intend to stay together it would be like having an affair, and I'm not cut out for affairs.'

'I wouldn't use your experience with Simon as a yard-stick. Put it this way——'

Gritting her teeth, she interrupted, 'Look, no matter how you put it, I do *not* want to sleep with you.'

'Liar,' he said calmly. 'If you hated the sight of me, found me physically repulsive, it would be different... But you don't, do you?'

'No,' she allowed reluctantly. 'But I've made up my mind I don't want to end up in your bed.'

Judging by his expression, he merely regarded opposition as fuel. 'Then I'll have to make you change your mind.'

'I won't do that,' she said with a certainty she was far from feeling. 'I intend to sleep alone.'

'A very virtuous resolution. But I don't believe you're taking into consideration the strength of the attraction between us——'

'But we don't *care* for each other,' she broke in desperately. 'I don't love you. You don't love me, do you?'

She found herself holding her breath, waiting for his answer with an almost painful intensity.

There was a barely perceptible hesitation, before he admitted, 'No, but I find you sweet and enchanting and delightfully sexy.'

'That's not enough.'

'It is for me.' His voice was sure and even. Purposefully, he drew her into his arms.

Gazing up at the ruthless beauty of his mouth, she started to tremble.

Taking her face between his palms, he moved his thumbs in a slow, semicircular motion that, as well as being masterful and mesmerising, had something of tenderness in it.

She found it impossible to move, impossible to breathe, impossible to think. What he was doing absorbed all her attention, held her spellbound.

He bent his peat-dark head and covered her face with butterfly kisses. The lightness of his touch only increasing the sensation, he let his mouth linger enticingly at the corner of hers before moving lower to where, with a tongue-tip, he traced the cleft in her chin, and the warm hollow at the base of her throat.

All around her the air tasted of fire and nectar, and a million bright stars showered down from the indigo sky.

After a moment his lips returned to play with hers, provoking, tantalising, coaxing them to part. When they did, he deepened the kiss and she was lost, the thrust of his tongue triggering off a devastating explosion of desire that destroyed any remaining resistance.

While he kissed her with masterful expertise his hands were travelling over her slender body, exploring enticing hollows and curves, leaving a trail of heated excitement in their wake.

Unnoticed almost, his deft fingers dealt with blouse buttons and the front fastening of her bra. Only when his mouth deserted hers and travelled over the perfumed curve of her breast did she appreciate she was half naked.

'You have beautiful breasts,' he murmured against her skin.

'Nothing you haven't seen before,' she reminded him with a tart flash of spirit, and felt, rather than heard, his laughter.

For a while he tormented and teased, wringing such ecstasy from her that she gasped and shuddered helplessly.

Then suddenly he was drawing away and she felt the night air cool against her damp skin. She opened dazed eyes to stare into his dark face.

'Well, Angel?' he asked softly. 'Do you want me?'

She wanted him more than anything in the world, more than she'd thought it possible to want any man. 'Yes.' Her whisper was a mere thread of sound.

'I didn't quite hear you.'

'Damn you,' she muttered. Then, unable to help herself, 'Yes, I want you.'

She saw the flash of white teeth as he smiled. A moment later she was swept triumphantly into his arms and borne into the house.

He set her down for a moment while he closed and locked the French windows. Then, lifting her again, he kissed her and, his lips clinging closely, carried her up the stairs.

CHAPTER SEVEN

ADAM put her down on the big bed and lifted his head to look at her. There was no need to switch on any lamps; the bedroom was awash with moonlight. It silvered his hard features and made his eyes gleam.

A perfumed night breeze wafted in to touch her cheek gently, and the sheet felt cool against her heated skin.

Bestowing many soft kisses and sensuous caresses that sent shivers of excitement running through her, Adam undressed her slowly and with care before deftly stripping off his own clothes and stretching full-length beside her.

When she reached out and would have pulled him to her he laughed softly, and said, 'Don't be so impatient, my Angel. We've got the whole night ahead of us.'

Using his fingers, his lips and tongue, and occasionally his teeth, he drove her slowly wild.

It was ravishment of the sweetest kind.

His mouth at her breast made her shudder and gasp until, unable to stand any more, she grasped a handful of his hair to hold him away, begging hoarsely, 'Oh, *please ...* Adam *...*'

Feeling his weight with a soaring rapture that transcended the merely physical, she had a sensation of utter *rightness*, of being one with this man.

Despite her eager acceptance of him, his first strong thrust made her cry out. She felt his big frame abruptly freeze into stillness, and a moment later he started to withdraw.

'No, no...' she whispered. 'It's all right.' Her arms wound tightly around his neck, she held on to him, pressing herself closer, moving her hips, the female in her knowing instinctively how to incite her male.

He gave a kind of groan, then began to move again, this time with much greater care.

Gladly she abandoned herself to the intense pleasure spiralling from a central molten core, a pleasure which built up and up until finally it overflowed into waves of ecstasy that rippled through her whole body and engulfed her mind.

When he lifted himself away and rolled on to his back, she lay motionless for a while, overwhelmed by the sheer joy and wonder of her first experience of physical love, before turning on her side and snuggling against him.

So deep was her euphoria that it took her a moment or two to realise he was lying quite still and unresponsive. Puzzled, she whispered, 'Adam?'

When he made no answer, she felt a sudden cold chill. Pushing herself up on one elbow, she peered at his face in the moonlight.

It was immediately apparent that he was quietly, but decidedly, *furious*.

'W-what is it?' she stammered. 'What's the matter?'

'I dislike being made a fool of,' he answered curtly.

'I—I don't understand what you're getting at.'

'You understand perfectly well what I'm getting at. You were a virgin.'

'Have you got something against virgins?' she asked, with an attempt at humour.

He wasn't amused. 'I understood that you and Simon had been lovers.'

'You mean you're sorry we hadn't?'

'I don't mean anything of the kind. I'm very glad you hadn't.'

Genuinely perplexed, she asked, 'Then why are you so angry?'

'Because you *deliberately* led me to believe the opposite.'

She couldn't deny the accusation. Swallowing, she said lamely, 'I'm sorry. But surely it doesn't *matter*?'

'Of course it matters,' he almost snarled.

Drawing away from him, she whispered, '*Why*? What difference does it make?'

'All the difference in the world. If I'd known the truth I wouldn't have taken you in the way I did.'

His manner suggested he wouldn't have taken her at all. Yet he was the one who had forced the issue...

'I don't suppose you were safeguarded?'

His sudden sharp question startled her. 'N-no,' she admitted.

'Believing that you'd had a lover, I presumed you would be.'

'Don't you know it's dangerous to presume anything?' With a spark of malice she used the same words he's used to her earlier that evening.

He glared at her, and she bit her lip, wishing she'd guarded her unruly tongue.

'So it's on the cards you might get pregnant.'

For a fleeting moment the thought of having Adam's child filled her with warmth. Then, like a douche of cold water, she recalled the *terms* of their marriage. If she *had* conceived he might feel tied to a relationship that he'd expected to be only temporary.

Was that why he was so angry? Did he think she'd deliberately set out to trap him?

Horrified, she hurried into a frantic denial.

Reaching out, he pulled her down beside him, and, putting a finger to her lips, halted the stumbling words. His voice gentle now, he assured her, 'I never thought that for a moment, Angel.'

She gulped, his unexpected kindness her undoing.

'Come on, now, there's no need to cry.' He used his thumb to wipe away the twin tears that had escaped and were trickling down her cheeks. 'I'm sorry, I've been a swine to you.' He sighed heavily. 'I should have stuck to our original agreement.'

'Why didn't you?' The question held confusion, all the bitterness of rejection.

'You're a young woman with normal, healthy feelings, a passionate woman with needs that aren't easy to suppress...'

He paused and appeared to be choosing his words carefully. 'And when someone's been used to having their needs fulfilled—as I thought *you* had—well, it becomes much harder to deny them. Several weeks ago you told me you were missing Simon——'

'I've asked you repeatedly to forget about Simon,' she cried.

'Making me believe he was your lover precluded that.' Levelly he added, 'You see, I couldn't be sure *you'd* forget him. I thought there was a distinct danger that in a few weeks you'd end up back in his bed, and I didn't want that to happen... For both our sakes, and to ensure peace and harmony in the home, it seemed much more sensible to make ours a real marriage, make sure it was *my* bed you slept in.'

It was her turn to be furious. So he'd set out to seduce her, not because he *wanted* her—she could have forgiven that, she conceded with grim humour—but simply because he'd been working from a false premise.

'Why, you arrogant... How dare you take it on yourself to decide whose bed...?' She spluttered to a halt, words failing her.

'I *am* your husband,' he pointed out calmly.

'In name only.'

'Oh, a little more than that, I think. When a marriage has been consummated——'

'It shouldn't have been consummated——'

'Given the circumstances, I'm inclined to agree. However, to employ a hackneyed phrase, what's done can't be undone.'

Pulling away, she began to wriggle out of bed. 'Perhaps not. But from now on I intend to use another room.'

He sat up and used a muscular arm to restrain her. 'Having burnt our boats, as far as I'm concerned it's in for a penny——'

'Really?' She struggled purposefully to free herself. 'As far as I'm concerned, it's once bitten——'

'Baby, you ain't seen nothing yet.' Tumbling her across his lap, he bent and began to mouth and bite her neck, making horrendous slurping, slobbering noises.

If his intention had been to defuse the situation, he succeeded. Unable to hold out against such absurd fooling, she began to giggle helplessly.

Sobering, he lay down again, pulling her with him, and, drawing her close, settled her head on his shoulder.

Gently he said, 'Try and get some rest now. I won't touch you again until we've had a chance to talk and resolve things. You'll be sleeping in my arms, nothing more.'

The words held an odd tenderness, and, despite everything, she experienced a sensation of warmth, of belonging.

But even if this closeness *seemed* right, it wasn't. The marriage had been made for all the wrong reasons.

Although she lay against him, feeling pleasure at the physical contact with his long, lean body, her heart was sad, melancholy as a wanderer who knew there was no way home. He didn't love her...

But she loved him ...

No...no! She couldn't allow herself to fall in love with her own husband, a man she'd proposed to solely for convenience.

Yet she *had*. Transfixed, she knew with a sudden startled flash of comprehension that she'd loved him from the start—even while she'd been telling herself that what she felt for him was purely physical.

Some people mistook lust for love, but, in her case, she realised with a kind of awe, it had been the opposite: she had mistaken love for lust.

She had warned herself that if she fell in love with him she could get badly hurt; still her heart filled with a soaring happiness, a paean of pure joy. No matter what the future held, she knew what it was like to really *love*, knew the glory of it.

Lying wide awake, she listened to Adam's quiet, even breathing, and tried to decide how best to handle this new and wonderful complication.

Feeling as she did, and having, as Adam had said, burnt her boats, she was willing to go on and make it not only a real marriage, but hopefully a *lasting* one.

The thing she mustn't do, the warning came swift and clear, was let him suspect she loved him. Knowing how she felt would put him in an impossible situation, pressurise him.

As would an unplanned pregnancy.

After a quick calculation she breathed a sigh of relief, convinced it was extremely unlikely that she would get pregnant from their lovemaking.

Though she could visualise Adam as a father—see him handling a baby with the same delicate sureness with which he'd handled her bridal bouquet—the choice of time, place and a *mother* for his children had to be his own.

All she could count on was a year. But if she couldn't make him love her in that time, then she never would...

And at the end of it, if he *did* walk away, at least she would have had a year of happiness. More than some people got in a lifetime...

So busy were her thoughts that it was almost two a.m. before her drooping lids shut out the cool silver room and she finally fell into an exhausted sleep.

She woke to a warm golden room and instant recollection. Gladness flooding through her, she turned her head. The place beside her was empty, a dented pillow the only proof that he'd ever been there.

No, not the only proof. Her body still sang with the satisfaction his lovemaking had given it. No woman could have had a more wonderful lover or a more blissful initiation into the delights of marriage.

Then, like a sting in the tail, came the rider: even if he had seduced her for the wrong reasons.

Pushing the thought away, she climbed out of bed and padded over to the window.

The pine-covered mountains made a glorious backdrop, and the smooth blue lake sparkled in the early morning sun. About fifty yards from the shore, a seal-dark head broke the water. She felt a queer tug at her heart as she realised the swimmer was Adam.

Eager to join him, she looked around for her case and discovered it had been put on a long, low chest beside his. The keys were in the lock, and her glasses, which Adam had removed the previous night, had been placed carefully on the lid.

Having located her sponge-bag, Angie hurriedly rummaged through the clothes that had been packed and unearthed a yellow one-piece swimsuit she'd had since school-days. She wrinkled her nose at it. It was hardly the most glamorous of garments, but as she had nothing better it would have to do.

After cleaning her teeth and taking a quick shower, she pulled it on, bundled her hair into a knot on top of her head, and, still barefoot, padded down to the beach.

The narrow strip of shingle, shielded on either side of rocky outcrops, was warm beneath her soles as she made her way down to the water's edge.

Wading in up to her waist, she gasped at the unexpected coldness of the water, before starting a careful breast-stroke.

Adam was doing an easy—but deceptively fast—crawl quite a distance out. He looked in his element. Which she definitely wasn't, most of her experience having been gained at the local baths.

Knowing her swimming was no match for his, she gave up the idea of trying to join him and stayed fairly close to the shore.

After a while, beginning to feel fatigued, she was about to start for the beach when he suddenly materialised by her side.

Treading water, he said coolly, 'Good morning. Sleep well?'

It wasn't exactly the rapturous greeting her unruly imagination had had in mind. All the same, she gave him a bright smile and answered, 'Yes, thank you.'

His hair was black and shining, plastered to his skull. In the sunlight his eyes gleamed a brilliant greeny-blue. Drops of water sparkled on his thick lashes and trickled down his tanned face.

He looked tough and healthy and so disturbingly attractive that her stomach tied itself in a knot.

'Enjoying your swim?'

'Oh, yes,' she answered a shade breathlessly. 'But the lake's colder than I'd expected.'

'Were you planning to stay in much longer?'

'No, I've had enough.'

Together they headed for the shore, Adam adjusting his pace to her much slower one. When they waded from the water, legs tired, she floundered a little, and he lent a strong right hand to pull her out.

She had hoped to walk up the beach hand in hand, but, to her disappointment, as soon as she found her footing he let her hand drop and turned away.

Becoming aware of the skimpiness of her wet costume, which pulled unbecomingly and flattened her breasts, Angie sighed, wishing she had something more glamorous to wear.

However, a quick sideways glance as they climbed the steps to the terrace showed that Adam was looking straight ahead and paying her not the slightest attention.

His skin gleamed, satiny-smooth and healthily bronzed. Wide shoulders and a powerful chest narrowed to a slim waist and taut stomach. Brief navy blue trunks clung to his lean hips, emphasising his masculinity.

Oh, but he was *beautiful*.

Her heart seemed to melt into pure molten gold, and her throat constricted. Swallowing, she looked hurriedly away, keeping her eyes firmly averted until they reached the villa.

As they crossed the landing at the top of the stairs, he said without inflexion, 'I take it you used the front bathroom, so I'll have one of the others.'

She hesitated, then, deciding to put her cards on the table, suggested boldly, 'Perhaps we could share.'

'I don't think so, Angel.'

His curt refusal was like a slap in the face.

Peeling off her wet costume, she tried to tell herself that Adam was just being meticulous. As soon as they'd had a chance to talk, everything would be all right.

But she remained strangely unconvinced.

When she'd showered, she went to find something to wear, wrapped in a large fluffy towel. Her case was exactly as she'd left it. Adam's had gone.

The instinct that had told her all was not well had obviously taken a very just view of the situation.

When she'd put on a beige and white striped cotton sundress and flat sandals, she brushed out her hair and, having found a circular clip in the box of make-up and accessories that Mrs Pimm had thoughtfully packed, fastened it in a ponytail.

Donning her glasses, she scowled at her reflection in the mirror. She looked like a well-scrubbed schoolgirl, when she would rather have looked like a *femme fatale*. Still, it was a bit early in the day to be going about in black satin and pearls, even if she'd had any.

She made her way down to the well-stocked kitchen and, having poured herself an orange juice, began to prepare breakfast, putting thin strips of streaky *pancetta* to crisp under the grill.

Still lamenting her lack of glamour, she was using a fork to vigorously beat eggs when there was a light slap on her vibrating backside, and Adam's amused voice remarked, 'Lady, you've left your motor running.'

'Watch it!' she warned with mock-belligerence, while her heart lifted. 'Molest the cook at your peril.'

'Wouldn't dream of it,' he assured her hastily, adding, 'Is there anything I can do to help?'

'I thought we'd eat on the terrace, if you'd like to take cutlery and things out.'

They breakfasted beneath the fringed umbrella, while birds sang and small speckled lizards sunned themselves on the warm balustrade only inches away.

From beneath her lashes she watched him quarter a peach and, face absorbed, neatly remove the stone before lifting one of the segments to his mouth.

She knew so little about him. What kind of childhood he'd had... How he'd come to stay in Australia for so long... Why he seemed almost to resent being *Sir Adam*... If there'd been many women in his life—though surely there *must* have been. And—her more immediate concern—why, apart from those few moments in the kitchen, he appeared to have deliberately withdrawn.

Anxious to know, she remarked as casually as possible, 'You said we needed to talk, resolve things...'

His dark head came up. 'They're already resolved,' he answered flatly. 'I should never have pressured you into a relationship you weren't prepared for and didn't really want.'

Glance level, he added, 'I can't give you back your virginity; all I *can* do is stick to the terms of our agreement from now on.'

'Suppose I say I don't *want* you to stick to them?'

With quiet authority he said, 'Leave it, Angel. I made a bad mistake in presuming you'd slept with Perry.'

'But shouldn't we at least discuss——?'

'There's nothing to discuss,' he broke in, his strong face implacable.

Her heart felt like lead. She'd lost her chance of keeping him, of making him love her.

It seemed ironical. If she *had* slept with Simon, she would probably have been in Adam's arms this very minute. Instead he was looking at her as though she were a troublesome child.

But she wasn't a child; she was a woman. Nothing to write home about, admittedly, but young and healthy and not *bad-looking*.

He'd said he found her sweet and enchanting and delightfully sexy, and when she'd denied that that was enough he'd assured her it was.

So *had* she lost her chance?

He was a man, when all was said and done. A red-blooded man...

His voice penetrated her brooding. She blinked, her golden eyes vague, oddly defenceless behind her owlish glasses. 'I'm sorry...?'

He gave her a narrow-eyed, assessing look, almost as if he could read her mind, then said with determined lightness, 'I thought we might perhaps catch a steamer and visit Bellazzo, one of the old monastic towns.'

'Oh... Yes, that would be lovely.'

And it *was* lovely, an outing filled with sunshine, warmth and *joie de vivre*, Adam once again proving himself to be fun, a friendly, stimulating companion.

The trouble was, she wanted so much *more* than friendly companionship. If they'd been brother and sister it would undoubtedly have rated as one of the happiest days of her life. But they weren't. They were man and wife.

Still, it was no use repining, Angie told herself firmly and, always a girl to make the most of what she *did* have, determined to enjoy herself.

After a morning spent walking around the narrow cobbled streets of the picturesque town, instead of going to a crowded trattoria for lunch they decided to picnic.

Sitting on some sun-baked stone steps, they ate slices of pizza and newly ripened figs with their fingers and drank Chianti from a straw-cradled bottle.

Afterwards they climbed to the top of the steps and, in a small *giardino publico*, stretched out on the warm grass beside a small marble fountain.

The combination of sun and wine and the splash of water induced a pleasant lethargy...

A gentle tug on her ponytail roused her. 'Wake up, sleepyhead, or you're going to be sunburnt.'

Lifting her cheek from Adam's chest, she pushed her glasses into place, blinking sleepily, then yawned, delicately as a cat.

She saw his expression change, but before she could decipher what emotion it held he jumped to his feet and, reaching for her hand, hauled her up.

Together they climbed a steep and dappled path, then several hundred steps, to the picturesque, white-walled Pino Monastery.

A huge bronze bell hung above the entrance arch, while a central well dominated the cobbled courtyard.

'Oh, look,' Angie exclaimed, peering over the thigh-high parapet to the still black water several feet below, 'I can see myself... I wonder how deep it is.'

Adam's reflection appeared beside her own. 'If you lean over any further you're liable to find out.'

'Those niches in the wall just above the water-line...' She pointed. 'What are they for?'

'That's where the monks used to store butter and milk and things they needed to keep cool.'

'Fascinating,' Angie breathed, craning at an even more perilous angle.

He took her arm in a firm grip. 'Yes, I always thought so.'

Righting herself, she asked, 'Then you've been to this monastery before?'

'Oh, yes, it used to be one of my favourite places. It's altered very little except that now, to raise money for the poor, they sell honey and home-made wine and open-air refreshments... Which isn't a bad idea... Fancy a coffee?'

'Love one.'

As luck would have it, they had the place to themselves. Sitting beneath a cool green canopy of vines, they were served with excellent coffee and amaretti by a cheerful, brown-robed, sandalled friar.

Nibbling one of the small, crisp macaroons, Angie watched Adam lift his cup to his lips then put it down again untasted.

For several minutes he sat gazing blindly into the middle-distance, as though his thoughts were trapped in the past and brought both mingled pain and gladness.

Her desire to understand him, to know what bitter-sweet memories made his expression so poignant, encouraged her to ask, 'I think you said you came to Como quite often as a child?'

Rousing himself, he glanced at her and answered evenly, 'Yes, I did. Usually during the school summer holidays.'

'And your parents come too?'

'My mother did. She loved it here.' Bitterly he added, 'Her marriage was a prison, her annual visit to Italy a parole, granted for good behaviour.'

There was a pause. Then as though, having once started, he felt the need to talk, he went on, 'Even as quite a young child I was aware that my father made her life hell.'

Angie waited, her troubled eyes fixed on his face.

'She was only eighteen when they met, but she'd inherited land adjoining Wingwood Hall and was rich in her own right... However, to give him his due, I don't think it was her money he was after. Though he was a widower more than twice her age, I believe he fell head over heels in love.

'Her mother, a social climber who thought a baronet was a good catch, ignored his reputation as a hard drinker and a gambler and pushed her into the marriage. I was born less than a year afterwards.

'When I was still a toddler she fell in love with Daniel Steele, a young architect who had been called in to draw up plans for a new wing to the Hall. He begged her to run away with him, but she wouldn't.

'Somehow my father found out. Steele was summarily dismissed and the wing never built. But especially for her, he *had* designed and built the little gazebo on the island she owned and loved.'

Adam's face softened. 'We used to escape there for an hour or so most days, just the two of us. She'd read me stories and we'd play games... She needed that escape. From then on my father's drinking and gambling got steadily worse, and he began to treat her like dirt...'

Thinking of the beautiful dark-haired woman with the sad eyes she'd met as a child, Angie wanted to weep. 'Why on earth did she stay with him?'

'She regarded her marriage vows as sacred, and I think she knew that, in a kind of queer, twisted way, he still loved her.

'Only on one occasion did she threaten to leave him. I was barely eight at the time, but old enough to know what was going on. When I tried to stand up for her he knocked me down.

'Normally she was quiet and gentle, but that day she turned on him like a fury. She told him if ever he lifted a finger to me again she would take me and go... He never did. But from then on he hated me, and treated her even worse.

'When the time came for me to go to boarding-school I didn't want to leave her, but she insisted I go. She was very strong in her own way.

'By the time I came of age there was no money left— in fact my father's debts were threatening to swamp us— so for my eighteenth birthday she gave me the island and the gazebo.'

How strange that they should each have been given the island as an eighteenth-birthday present, Angie thought wonderingly.

But he was continuing, 'When I finished university I went home to live for her sake, but I soon realised my presence only aggravated matters. I pleaded with her to leave him, but she steadfastly refused. That was when I threw in my hand and went to Australia.

'I'd been growing sugar-cane in Queensland for a couple of years when she had a fall from her horse and broke her neck. She'd been dead and buried six weeks before my father told me.

'There didn't seem much point in going home then...'

Hearing the bitter despair behind his quiet statement, the sadness and guilt, the unending anguish, Angie's heart bled for him. It was plain that after all this time he still blamed himself for abandoning his mother.

'That was when I moved to South Australia. Somehow I felt restless, unable to settle down to farming again...'

There was a long silence, then Adam sighed. 'You're the only person I've ever told all that to.'

'I'm sorry if I——'

He shook his head, cutting off her apology. 'Talking about things is a bit like lancing a septic wound,' he said wryly. 'It hurts like hell, but it lets the poison out and makes the patient feel better.'

It also explained a great deal: why he appeared to resent his title; why a lot of his memories had seemed to be dark ones; why he'd been so set on having the island back...

Well, he *should* have it back, she vowed, as soon as it was legally hers to give.

They returned to town on one of the ponies and traps plying for hire, and, as though it *had* done him good to get things out of his system, Adam seemed both cheerful and carefree. And depressingly *friendly*.

When a blue velvet dusk descended he took her to a lakeside restaurant with a small open-air orchestra. Listening to the drifting strains of Neapolitan love-songs, they dined on the terrace, where fireflies danced in the warm, scented air.

Even in this most romantic of settings, to Angie's unspoken chagrin Adam's behaviour remained determinedly avuncular.

After the meal they stood by the rail for a while, watching the lights of a fishing boat and enjoying the slight breeze that night had brought.

A flying insect landed on Angie's neck, and Adam leaned closer to blow it away. A shiver of excitement ran through her. Taking advantage of his nearness, she slipped her hand into his.

Returning it to her like an unwanted Kleenex, he said severely, 'Behave yourself, Angel.'

All evening he'd been treating her like a schoolgirl, she fumed, a child taken out to a grown-up restaurant for a treat. But just wait until they got back to the villa; she'd show him whether she was a child or not!

CHAPTER EIGHT

IT WAS very late before they got back to Menezzo, but, the adrenalin still flowing, fuelling her nervous energy, Angie opted for walking from the landing-stage instead of taking a taxi.

Apparently doubting her motives for suggesting a moonlight stroll, Adam kept a careful foot of space between them, inciting afresh her resolve to *make* him want her, come what may.

When they reached the villa he let them in and asked in a polite, no-nonsense manner, 'A brandy on the terrace? Or would you prefer to go straight to bed?'

'Oh, straight to bed, I think,' she answered sweetly. 'But you have a brandy by all means.'

He shot her a wary glance, as though wondering at her dulcet tones. 'Goodnight, then.'

'Goodnight,' she cooed, and headed up the stairs.

Moving unhurriedly, but with purpose, she stripped off and showered before cleaning her teeth and brushing her ash-blonde hair into a long, shining fall.

The only eau-de-toilette she had with her was Lily of the Valley. Wishing it were Chanel, she splashed it on liberally.

Then, searching through her case, she decided the most seductive garment it contained was a coffee-coloured dressing-gown in a fine, silky material.

When she'd tied the belt she was pleased to see that it moulded itself lovingly to every curve, and was cut so that it gave more than a glimpse of the shadowy valley between her breasts.

Leaving her glasses in the bedroom, barefoot, heart beating fast, she made her way down the stairs.

He was standing by the balustrade within the range of the villa's lights, tension in his neck and shoulders, looking up the lake. Though she made not the slightest sound, some sixth sense must have prompted him to turn.

'I've changed my mind,' she purred, moving to join him. 'I will have that brandy after all.'

With an effort he dragged his eyes away from the clinging gown and, his mouth a grim line, went into the house and returned with a glass for her.

'Thank you.' Putting it on the balustrade, she gave him a teasing glance from beneath long lashes.

He folded his arms across his chest, his flagrant masculinity an unspoken threat, and studied her air of honeyed provocation. 'What the hell are you up to?' he demanded.

'Up to?' she echoed with wide-eyed innocence, knowing she'd disturbed his calm, and glad of it. 'What makes you think I'm up to something?'

'All this sweetness, when you've been seething for most of the evening.'

'So you noticed?'

He grinned briefly at her tone. 'Couldn't fail to. You're very transparent.'

Stung, she accused, 'You've been treating me like a child. But I'm not a child; I'm a woman.'

She half turned, and with a sultry glance contrived to brush her breast against his arm, before giving him a better view of her cleavage by leaning forward to rest her elbows on the stone coping.

To her utter mortification, he threw back his head and burst out laughing. 'Oh, Angel,' he spluttered, 'you're not cut out to be a temptress.'

He was still laughing when he saw the tears on her cheeks. His mirth vanished instantly, and, murmuring something beneath his breath, he started to draw her towards him.

Bitterly hurt and humiliated by the knowledge that she wasn't even attractive enough to tempt him, that he was *laughing* at her, she tore herself free and bolted.

Halfway across the lounge he caught her wrist, stopping her headlong flight.

'Leave me alone.' When he tried to pull her into his arms, a primitive fury she was to be thoroughly ashamed of afterwards made her fight like a wildcat, clawing and kicking.

Her nails raked down his cheek, and he muttered an oath. The next second her feet were swept from under her and she landed flat on her back on the carpet, taking Adam with her.

Still she fought, writhing and squirming until, having caught her wrists and pinned them above her head, he used the weight of his body to hold hers down.

'Gently, now, gently.' His face, slightly blurred, was only inches from hers. She could see the gleam of his eyes through the thick dark lashes, the flare of his nostrils, the arrogant beauty of his mouth.

Her breath coming fast, she turned her head away.

'Look at me, Angel.'

Biting her lip, she kept her head stubbornly turned.

'Well, *listen* then. I didn't mean to hurt your feelings. Believe me, you don't need to play the siren to tempt me. You're quite tempting enough. Why else do you think I treated you as a child? If I hadn't, I wouldn't have been able to keep my hands off you.' He bent and let his lips follow the clean curve of her jaw. 'Tell me you forgive me.'

'I *don't*,' she said fiercely. 'You seduced me because you thought Simon had been my lover, then you were furious because I was still a virgin. You suggested that, having burnt our boats, it was "in for a penny", then, deciding it had been a mistake after all, you changed your mind—a unilateral decision in which I'd apparently no say whatsoever.'

'I've treated you badly, I admit. But I want to——'

'Doesn't it matter a toss what *I* want?' she interrupted.

For a moment he was quite still, looking down into her flushed face, with its generous mouth and cleft chin. Then, softly, he asked, 'What *do* you want, Angel?'

When she didn't answer, he began to make rhythmic movements with his pelvis, imitating the thrust of possession. 'This?'

Her pulses began to race, and desire ran like liquid fire through her veins.

Then, showing he himself was far from unaffected, he muttered hoarsely, 'As things are, I don't want you to get pregnant...'

'I'm fairly safe on that score.'

'Nor do I want to get you...hooked on sex.'

'Too late.' She gave a little choke of laughter. 'We seem to have come full circle. You seduced me because you thought, wrongly, that my sexual appetite had been roused... Now it *has*, you're refusing to gratify that hunger.'

She laughed again, harshly. 'Wouldn't it be funny if I ended up in Simon's bed after all?' Her last remark, calculated to infuriate him, succeeded beyond her wildest dreams.

His teeth came together with a snap, then he snarled, 'If you're visualising keeping anyone's bed warm it had better be mine.'

She decided to goad the lion. 'Having thought about it, I'm afraid I don't fancy a reluctant lover——'

'Why, you little——!'

'I may not rate as a temptress, but at the very least I want a man who shows some enthusiasm——'

The last word ended in a little gasp as he nuzzled aside her wrap and put his mouth to her breast. Deliberately he set out to drive her mad, keeping her wrists imprisoned when she would have put a stop to such exquisite torment.

When she was nothing but a quivering mass of sensations he stripped off his clothes and took her with unrestrained passion and scant regard for her inexperience.

It was like being caught and tossed body and soul in a whirlpool of feeling from which she emerged spent and shattered.

She was unaware of the tears trickling down her face until his anguished voice begged, 'Don't cry... For God's sake don't cry. I'm sorry I lost control, sorry if I hurt you.'

From when she was a child she'd rarely cried and, when she had, her tears had usually been caused by some powerful emotion other than pain. Sadness sometimes, anger occasionally, but, more often, happiness.

Now she was weeping for pure joy.

Lifting himself away, he sat up and gathered her to him, cradling her head against his chest with a rough tenderness that showed how disturbed he was.

He really didn't know how she felt, how marvellous it had been to be treated not as some china doll that might break, but as an equal partner, a woman to his man.

His anxiety was so ludicrous that she gave a husky laugh.

As if he couldn't believe his ears, he held her away a little to study her face. 'What's so funny?' he demanded.

In a muffled voice she told him, 'You.'

He looked so taken aback that she had a job not to laugh again. 'Oh? And why is that precisely?'

She smiled at him through her tears. 'Far from hurting me, it was the most wonderful experience of my life.'

Shaken to the core, he stared at her. Then with an incoherent murmur he drew her close and, his lips muffled against her silky hair, held her so tightly that she thought her ribs might crack. Still she revelled in it.

After a moment his grip loosened, and, drawing away a little, he kissed her gently.

Noticing the scratches on his cheek, she traced them with a penitent finger, and, bitterly reproaching herself for her lack of control, whispered, 'I'm so sorry.'

Taking her hand, he kissed each finger and then the palm. 'I'm the one who should be sorry. So far I seem to have made all the wrong decisions, drawn all the wrong conclusions...'

When she failed to comment, he released her and moving away, deliberately avoiding bodily contact, and asked, 'So where do we go from here?'

'I'd like to go to bed,' she answered simply.

'Alone, or with me?'

Of course, he was asking so much more, asking about a year's commitment.

He was watching her, his dark face expressionless, making it clear that the decision was hers to make, and hers alone.

She knew quite well what she wanted, but second thoughts had highlighted the enormity of the risk she would be taking.

Her commitment, though he didn't know it, would be so much greater than his. To him it would mean living together with only the lightest of emotional ties. To her it would mean *everything*. And at the end of that year he might walk away.

At best it would be an insecure stability.

'With you,' she said softly.

The rest of their honeymoon was idyllic: long golden days spent walking, driving, sightseeing, or just lazing by the lake and reading; long starlit nights spent making love or lying contentedly in each other's arms.

But they were fascinated by each other's minds as well as bodies, and they talked a lot, finding it fun to match wits, to strike intellectual sparks off each other.

If there was such a thing as heaven on earth, Angie had found it, and she never wanted their honeymoon to end.

But end it did.

They arrived home to misty rain and the lushness of an English summer, which seemed particularly green and luxuriant after the sun-baked countryside they had left behind them.

When they reached Fife Cottage Adam drew the car to the side of the track and, leaving their cases in the boot, came round to help Angie out.

It had stopped raining now, and the air was fresh and sweet. As she glanced towards Clouds, standing serene in the watery sun, she was suddenly gripped by the strangest unease, a *premonition* that something was very wrong. She shivered uncontrollably.

'Cold?' Adam asked, surprised.

'No, no... Just someone walking over my grave.'

Mrs Pimm was out, but Tosca, who looked fat and well satisfied with life, gave them her usual warm welcome.

Still the unaccountable feeling of foreboding was there, and growing stronger. As though the previous three weeks had been just a happy dream, and she'd awakened to unpleasant reality, Angie felt alarmed, uncertain of herself and the future.

Making a determined effort to regain her self-possession, she said briskly, 'I'd better go next door and get organised... if you know where the keys are kept.'

'In here.' Adam opened the top drawer of the dresser and glanced inside. 'But they seem to be missing...'

When, noticing an odd, inexplicable note of tension in his voice, she looked at him quickly, he added, 'Which might mean Mrs Pimm is round there now, getting the place ready for us.'

Though he spoke lightly, she had the strangest feeling that he too was waiting for something awful to happen.

Dropping an arm around Angie's shoulders, he accompanied her out the front way, Tosca at their heels.

As they walked up the drive to Clouds an Air Force jet ripped the sky apart with a sound like tearing cloth, and a swallow, its beak full of insects, swooped low over their heads.

Confirming Adam's conjecture, the door to Clouds stood a little ajar. He gave Angie a quick, reassuring smile and, sweeping her into his arms, carried her over the threshold.

Still holding her, he bent to kiss her. Their lips met and clung. What started out as a light kiss had become decidedly more ardent when the living-room door opened, and a woman's brittle voice announced, 'I was expecting you. I heard your car arrive a short while ago...'

Angie squirmed a little, but Adam unhurriedly finished what he'd begun before lifting his head.

Pushing her glasses into place and focusing on the woman who, dressed in white silk trousers and a scarlet top, was standing watching them, Angie gasped. 'Paula... What a surprise!'

Looking not at Angie, but at Adam, Paula said, 'Yes, it is, rather. Still, you've always been something of a dark horse.'

Ignoring this somewhat cryptic statement, Angie asked, 'But what on earth are you doing here?'

'Being bored out of my mind, sister, dear.'

Immaculately groomed, her oval face perfectly made up, Paula kept her attention focused on Adam. 'I hope you don't object, but, as you weren't home, I put my car in your garage and borrowed your housekeeper to clean and cook for me.'

Putting Angie down, and keeping a steadying arm around her waist until she found her feet, Adam enquired idly, 'And where is that good lady?'

'She's taken the bus into town to do some shopping for me...'

Suddenly her gaze moved to a spot behind him, and, with an abrupt sharpening of tone, she exclaimed, 'For God's sake get that creature out of here...'

Angie turned her head to see the bull-terrier ambling in.

'You know I can't stand dogs!' Paula exclaimed. 'Get it *out*!'

'I'll put her in the kitchen if you like,' Angie offered.

'You'll do no such thing. While I'm living here that animal stays outside.'

As though understanding every word, the fawn and white bitch slunk out, ears flat, tail clapped between her legs.

His expression non-committal, hiding what he was thinking, Adam closed the door behind her.

Anxiety lying like a lump of lead in her stomach, Angie asked through dry lips, 'What do you mean, "living here"?'

Paula allowed herself a smile, something she seldom did, because of the risk of wrinkles. 'I was married two days before you were, so, under the terms of Ben's will, Clouds now belongs to me.'

Angie stood as though transfixed. She felt sick and stunned, her brain numb with shock. Not only could she not save Ben's beloved house, but she couldn't give Adam the island.

'Is your husband with you?' It was Adam who asked the question.

'You must be joking! Ross absolutely *detests* the country—he couldn't even bring himself to stay for a few weeks—and as——'

'Perhaps we could sit down,' Adam broke in politely but peremptorily, after a glance at Angie's pinched face, paper-white beneath the tan. 'This has come as a bit of a shock.'

'Of course.' With an unmistakable air of being in possession—and possession being nine-tenths of the law—Paula led the way into the living-room.

Adam steered Angie to the nearest chair and pushed her gently into it. Then with a kind of easy arrogance he stood by the flower-filled hearth, legs a little apart, facing the other woman. 'You were saying your husband detests the country. Doesn't that make things difficult for you?'

She gave him a glance full of meaning. 'You're no fool, and you must know the score, so why play with words? My marriage was a business arrangement, pure and simple.'

With barely concealed resentment she added, 'At this very moment my "husband" is in the South of France, living it up.'

His air one of urbane detachment, Adam queried, 'But surely one of the conditions is that he lives here with you?'

'On paper. But my solicitor says that, so long as we are *technically* living here, it's not necessary for either of us to do so *in fact*—if our jobs happen to take us abroad, for instance... All I really need is a valid marriage certificate.'

A sudden shaft of sunlight falling across his face made him narrow his eyes, turning them into gleaming slits. 'Do go on.'

Her shoulders lifted in a slight shrug. 'As far as I'm concerned, that's all there is to it. I was married first and the property's mine. In a week or two, when everything's settled, I'll be a free woman again.'

Leaning idly against the mantelpiece, a lock of dark hair falling over his forehead, his hands in his pockets, Adam studied her. 'And you won't be staying?'

'In this dead-alive hole? Do me a favour, darling. I'll never know how Angie stands it.'

Quietly he said, 'She loves it...'

And Adam loved the island. Angie felt as if she were mortally wounded, slowly bleeding to death.

'This is her home and she loves it.'

Paula spread slim hands in a dismissive gesture. 'If she'd still been single I would have let her stay on for another year as caretaker—someone will have to look after the place until it can be sold.' Turning to Angie, she said shortly, 'But as things are, I presume you won't want to.'

Thrown, totally disconcerted, Angie hesitated.

Instantly the blue eyes widened. 'Or am I mistaken? I met your erstwhile fiancé one day in town, and he told me some interesting things...

'At the time I put it down to rancour—he was certainly over the moon when he discovered that I'd got in first on the marriage stakes—but perhaps he spoke the truth after all...'

Watching the colour flood into Angie's cheeks, Paula exclaimed with malicious glee, 'What a scream! Though I was intrigued by the last-minute switch in bridegrooms, I didn't think you had it in you to buy yourself a husband——'

'You're quite wrong,' Adam informed her. 'In my case, at least, it was love at first sight.'

'Oh, come off it,' Paula said inelegantly. 'Angie's a nice enough girl, but hardly the kind of raving beauty to inspire instant devotion.'

'Perhaps you know the old saying about beauty being in the eye of the beholder?' Adam enquired smoothly. Then, with a touch of cold hauteur, 'And what makes you imagine I can be bought?'

A shade uncertainly, Paula said, 'Simon told me that all you'd inherited was an old hall that's mouldering away and a huge pile of debts.'

'I must have a few words with that gentleman.' Though he spoke mildly enough, the look on Adam's face boded ill for Simon.

Gathering herself, Angie said, 'And I'd like a word with Paula. Alone, if you don't mind.'

'Of course I don't mind.' But the sudden glint of wariness in his eyes belied the easy acceptance. Stooping, he kissed her lightly but proprietorially, before turning to go.

In the doorway he paused to say, 'While you're here, Angel, if you'd like to gather together your clothes and personal belongings, when I come back I'll help you move them.'

On the surface it was a casual offer of assistance, but Angie sensed the steel running through it and knew that in reality it was both a command and a warning.

When the front door had closed behind him Paula said, 'OK, so what's the score?'

Angie looked her in the eye. 'I want to keep the island. It was my eighteenth-birthday present from Ben.'

'On your bike!' Paula retorted with a laugh. 'It's part of the estate.' Sharply she added, 'Unless you've got legal documents that prove otherwise.'

'No, I haven't,' Angie admitted.

The blue eyes were triumphant. 'Then it's tough luck.'

Trying to keep calm, Angie asked, 'Well, will you *sell* it to me?'

'Sell it to you?'

'I'll pay you every penny of its market value.'

'When?'

'As soon as I can... A bit at a time, the minute I find a job...'

'Forget it,' Paula advised flatly. 'I want it now in a lump sum, not in dribs and drabs.'

'But surely you can't *need* the money straight away? You'll have whatever the house and the rest of the land brings... Oh, *please*, Paula.'

'Perhaps if I knew *why* you wanted it so badly...' Paula's eyes gleamed with curiosity.

Deciding that her only hope was to tell the truth, Angie disregarded Adam's tacit warning, and said obliquely, 'You were quite right, incidentally.'

'About what?'

'I did ask Adam to marry me.'

Paula gave a little crow of mirth. 'So he *was* only being chivalrous... I thought as much... But how the hell did you get him to agree? No matter what your ex-fiancé says about him being in financial difficulties, he doesn't look to me like a man you could offer money to... Even if you had any...'

'No.'

'So what *did* you offer him?'

'I promised to give him the island.' The words came out in a rush.'

When Paula looked blank, Angie explained, 'It's a part of the Wingwood estate that Adam badly wants back.'

Raising her thin, carefully plucked brows, Paula chortled. 'And now it's not yours to give. What a hoot!'

Hands clenched into fists, Angie persisted desperately, 'But he's kept his part of the bargain and I've just *got* to keep mine.'

There was a stunned silence, then, 'My God,' Paula exclaimed, 'I do believe you're in love with the man!'

Betraying colour poured into Angie's face.

'Well, isn't that rich! Though not really surprising.' A strange heated excitement in her eyes, Paula added, 'He's a gorgeous brute by any standard.'

Vexed that she'd given herself away, Angie tried to get back to the point. 'Look, can't you give me time to pay? You're a high wage earner, right at the top of your profession; surely—— '

'For heaven's sake don't be so naïve,' Paula snapped. 'I'm right at the top now, but in a year or two I won't be. New faces—*younger* faces—come along, and I don't intend to fade quietly into obscurity.

'As soon as I see the writing on the wall I'm going to get out of modelling and buy into the fashion business. For that I'll need every cent I can lay my hands on, and I——'

She broke off as a tap at the door heralded the entrance of a small, stout body clutching an array of plastic carriers.

'Sorry I've been so long, Miss Pleydell,' the newcomer addressed Paula, 'but I missed the four-thirty bus and had to wait an hour.'

'That's all right, Mrs Pimm,' Paula said magnanimously.

To cope with the vagaries of the British summer, Mrs Pimm was dressed in a knobbly tweed coat and a felt hat from under which wisps of grey hair were escaping. She had a pleasant, sensible face, saved from dullness by a pair of humorous hazel eyes.

Putting the various bags down, she turned to Angie. 'I've just spoken to Sir Adam, Lady Wingwood, and he said I was to start helping you move your clothes and things.'

Thrown by being addressed as Lady Wingwood, Angie stammered, 'I—I haven't had time to collect them . . .'

'You don't need to move out straight away if you don't want to,' Paula offered, adding derisively, 'Bearing in mind the circumstances . . .'

Angie bit her lip. There was no way she could stay here and become a butt for Paula's unkind humour. 'I think it would be better if I did,' she replied with what calmness she could muster.

'Well, then I'll come and give you a hand,' Mrs Pimm said comfortably. 'With Miss Pleydell's permission, that is.'

Paula shrugged. 'Free free.' Taking a fashion magazine from one of the carriers, she began to flick through it.

In a kind of stupor, Angie went upstairs and, while Mrs Pimm trotted backwards and forwards between the two cottages, carrying armfuls of clothes and shoes, began to gather together her relatively few personal possessions.

Undies, night-wear and other odds and ends she put into an old suitcase, along with a framed photograph of Ben.

Not until her familiar room wore the stripped, impersonal look of a hotel bedroom did it strike Angie that she was leaving for good.

But it wasn't only Clouds she'd lost . . .

Her knees turning to jelly, she sat down abruptly on the edge of the bed.

She had also lost Adam.

And it had happened so suddenly. Almost before the honeymoon was over, before they could begin any kind of normal life together, their agreement had become null and void. Without a year's grace to try and make him love her, everything was, to all intents and purposes, over between them.

The realisation spawned almost unbearable anguish, as well as bringing home the dismal practicalities of the situation.

She was jobless and had nowhere to live. The best she could hope for was to find a cheap bed-sit. But if she did, what would happen to Tosca and Barnaby and poor Nicholas?

Everyone seemed to have taken it for granted that, for the moment at least, she would move next door. But Fife Cottage had only one bedroom, and presumably Mrs Pimm slept in there.

So where did that leave *her*? Or Adam, for that matter? *He'd* been expecting to move into Clouds...

Dear God, she loved him so...

And she couldn't even give him the island...

The knowledge that she'd failed him in that was like a bruise on her soul.

Haphazard thoughts still ricocheting round her mind like stray bullets, she became aware that she wasn't alone, and lifted a stricken face.

'Don't take it so hard,' Adam said urgently. 'It's not the end of the world.'

But it was.

Somehow she smiled and said, 'Of course not. It just came as a bit of a shock.'

He touched her cheek with a gentle palm. 'That's my girl.'

When he picked up the case, without a single backward glance, she went ahead of him down the stairs on legs that felt curiously stiff and alien, as if they didn't belong to her.

Paula was waiting in the hall. Her flawless face knowing, slightly mocking, she said to Adam, 'I did tell

Angie that *in the circumstances* she could stay on for a while if she wanted to...'

Anger flashed in his eyes, then was quickly veiled. 'How kind of you,' he said with ironic courtesy.

'But she refused.' After a pregnant pause Paula continued, 'It occurred to me her decision might... well...make things a little difficult.'

His face impassive, he agreed, 'There is a slight problem. Wingwood Hall isn't yet ready for occupation and, as you probably know, my cottage has only one bedroom. So someone will need to move out.'

'Well, there's a bed here for you.' Her significant little smile left no doubt as to *whose* bed.

'Thank you. Though it wasn't of myself I was thinking. Having a wife, I don't at present need a housekeeper, and as Mrs Pimm's been taking care of you I thought you might like to retain her services...' The words flowed like liquid honey over a warm spoon. 'So it makes sense for her to stay here.'

Just for an instant Paula's face showed her chagrin, before it became a beautiful mask.

'I'll continue to pay her wages, of course.' Though Adam's expression was bland, his last words held a sting, and Paula's scarlet lips thinned.

Turning solicitously to Angie, he asked, 'Have you got everything you need for the present?'

Feeling almost sorry for Paula, she said steadily, 'Yes, I think so. The only things left are my books and one or two oddments.'

'Ready for home, then, Angel?'

His warm, intimate tone, his use of the word 'home', his pretence that they still had a relationship, nearly proved to be her undoing. Unable to speak for the tears that threatened, she nodded.

He opened the door and ushered her out, turning at the last moment to give Paula an ironic little salute and say, 'I'll make sure Mrs Pimm's round in time to cook your supper.'

As the door was slammed behind them, with his free hand he took Angie's arm in a grip that, though light, was like a steel manacle.

Startled, she glanced at him, and caught her breath. The veneer of urbanity had vanished. His face was set, his mouth a hard line, and his greeny-blue eyes had darkened to the turbulent jade of a raging sea.

There was no doubt that he was absolutely *livid*. *And with her*.

Miserably she admitted he had every right to be furious. She didn't blame him in the least. He'd lost the island, married her for nothing, and, because she'd deliberately misled him, made it impossible to have the marriage annulled. Now a divorce was the only option open to him.

Drained and spent, without defences, she felt a cowardly impulse to run.

But even if she could break free, where was there to run to?

Knowing she had no alternative but to stay and face his anger, she lifted her head, squared her shoulders, and preceded him into Fife Cottage.

CHAPTER NINE

THE appetising smell of grilling chops greeted them, and Mrs Pimm, wearing a spotless sprigged apron, came bustling out of the small kitchen to say obligingly, 'I can dish up straight away if you're ready to eat.'

His urbane mask firmly back in place, Adam said, 'We'll be ready as soon as I've taken Angel's case up.'

At the door to the stairs he paused. 'By the way, I've arranged for you to stay with Ms Pleydell and keep house for her until things are sorted out. I hope you've no objection.'

'It's a weight off my mind,' she assured him at once. 'With so much happening out of the blue, like it has, I didn't quite know where I was.'

Turning to Angie, she explained a shade apologetically, 'I was going to let you know when your sister turned up, but she asked me not to. She said it was meant to be a surprise.'

It had certainly been that, Angie was thinking, when an odd recollection popped into her head. Adam hadn't seemed surprised. It was almost as if he'd been *expecting* Paula to be there.

They sat at a table in front of the open window and ate in silence, while Mrs Pimm scurried about, moving her belongings next door.

Low evening sun slanted across the garden, making long shadows, and on the topmost branch of the lilac bush a blackbird sang his heart out while, sitting on the warm, flagged path, Tosca stretched her sturdy neck and scratched ruminatively.

Angie risked a glance in Adam's direction, hoping to catch his eye and say something to ease the tension, to mitigate the coming storm. But, his dark face stern and aloof, he looked so unapproachable that her courage failed her.

Worry, lying like a rock in the pit of her stomach, took away her appetite, but she made a valiant effort to force down some of the food so as not to hurt the housekeeper's feelings.

'There, now.' That good lady appeared with a tray of coffee and, having filled both their cups, announced, 'I've left everything spick and span, so if there's nothing else you're wanting I'll go and take care of Miss Pleydell.'

'No, nothing else, thank you, Gladys,' Adam said pleasantly.

'Then I'll be off.'

Toying with her coffee, Angie waited for him to speak, to lay the blame fairly and squarely at her door and give free rein to his fury.

Instead he got up to close the window, first whistling the bull-terrier who, with her crocodile grin and rolling, bow-legged gait, came obediently up the path.

Leaving his coffee untouched, he let the dog in and took her through to the kitchen before locking and bolting both doors with great deliberation.

'What are you doing?' Angie, trying to sound casual, only succeeded in sounding apprehensive.

'Preparing for an early night,' Adam said coolly.

'But we haven't... I mean... we need to talk.'

'We can talk tomorrow.'

She shook her head. 'We can't just go to bed as if nothing had happened, with nothing settled.'

His greeny-blue eyes, bright with suppressed rage, were fixed on her unblinkingly. 'What is there to settle?'

Feeling menaced by his look and by his imposing height, she jumped to her feet and faced him. Afraid, not so much of him, but of her own vulnerability to his anger, she blurted out, 'You know perfectly well.'

'The only thing I know is you're my wife and I want to take you to bed.'

'I'd rather we talked.' A shade wildly, she added, 'I'm sorry about the island. I wish I'd never involved you in all this. You haven't...' Pulling herself up, she made a clumsy attempt to re-phrase what she'd been about to say. '*Neither* of us has got what we hoped for, and you're... *we're* stuck with a marriage we didn't really want. The whole thing's been a complete fiasco...'

He went white beneath his tan, and she realised her attempt at an apology seemed only to have made matters worse.

His voice cold as melt-water, he demanded, 'Is that what you think?'

'Well, hasn't it?'

Legs a little apart, arms folded across his chest, he queried, 'So what do you suggest we do about it?'

'I don't know what we *can* do,' she admitted. Then, bravely, 'Except get a divorce as soon as possible.' Seeing an expression cross his face that could have been mistaken for pain, she stammered, 'W-what do *you* want to do about it?'

Savagely he said, 'At the moment, as we *are* still married, I'd like to go to bed and exercise a husband's prerogative. Or would you rather I went next door?'

A whiplash couldn't have hurt more.

Looking down at the shabby, rose-patterned carpet, she said miserably, 'I don't wonder you're angry. I know I'm to blame for the whole sorry mess. If I hadn't been so desperate to keep Clouds...'

'Of course you're not to blame,' he disagreed curtly.

With a sudden hope, her head came up and her golden eyes widened behind the dark-rimmed owlish glasses. 'I-I thought you were angry with *me*.'

'I *am* angry with you.' The look on his lean, saturnine face left her in no doubt that that was an understatement. 'So angry, in fact, I'm very tempted to put you over my knee.'

When she flinched away, he went on coldly, 'But as I've never struck a woman in my life, and don't intend to start now, I'm going to get rid of my frustrations by taking you to bed and making love to you.'

Much as she loved him, she wasn't going to bed with him on those terms; it was degrading, soul-destroying.

Out of her hurt, she mocked, '"Making love"? Is *that* what you call it? And if the only reason is to vent your anger, I'd sooner you beat me,' she added passionately.

'I doubt it.' Smiling like a tiger, he advanced on her purposefully.

Breath coming fast, heart pounding with sledgehammer blows, she tried to keep him at bay with words. 'I don't understand... If you don't think I'm to blame, *why* are you so angry with me?'

'I'll give you one guess.' He was much too close, making her palms grow clammy and fine perspiration break out on her forehead.

Lifting her chin, she informed him haughtily, 'I'm not in the mood for guessing games.'

'Neither am I.' His eyes glinted green as a cat's. 'So perhaps you'll tell me exactly what you said to that harpy next door.'

'Oh...' Realising the cause of his anger, Angie's hand flew to her mouth. Then, trying hard not to sound defensive, she said, 'I simply told her the truth.'

'So you simply told her the truth...' Savagely he mimicked her insouciant tone. 'Why, in God's name?'

'I... Well, I...' She floundered, unwilling to explain about the island.

Silkily Adam suggested, 'Perhaps you thought you'd get rid of me.'

'Get rid of you?' Angie echoed blankly.

'It can't have escaped your notice that from the word go she's been . . . shall we be polite and say *interested* in me as a man.'

Unable to admit to the fierce jealousy she'd felt, Angie stayed silent.

'Did you think that as, *in the circumstances*——' he used the hated phrase with undisguised bitterness '—I was no further use to you you could pass me on like some unwanted commodity?'

As she gaped at him, he said with dangerous mildness, 'Well, let me make something quite plain. *You* were the one to suggest this marriage, but *I'll* be the one to decide when it ends. So if you were planning to ditch me and rush off to Perry for comfort——'

Her face bloodless, she denied, 'I wasn't planning any such thing.'

'That's just as well.' He curved a hand lightly around her throat, his thumb moving caressingly over the soft skin beneath her jaw. 'Because, having got this far, I've no intention of being cuckolded. Now come to bed.'

Cold inside, she said shakily, 'I don't want to come to bed. I won't let you "make love" to me merely as a release for anger.'

His white teeth flashed in a cruel smile. 'How do you propose to stop me?'

Biting her lip, she made no reply.

Watching the small, betraying movement, he asked, 'So are you going to walk upstairs, or do I have to carry you?'

Knowing she must keep her self-control at all costs, chin up, back ramrod-straight, she went ahead of him up the narrow wooden stairs and across the landing.

The bedroom was surprisingly pleasant, with a faded hand-made counterpane on the high, old-fashioned bed, a jug of sweet peas on the well-polished chest of drawers, and a couple of sheepskin rugs on the oak floorboards.

Mrs Pimm appeared to have unpacked and put everything away, and Angie's nightdress and dressing-gown lay on the bottom of the bed. Both the windows were open wide, letting in the cool evening air.

In the middle of the room Angie turned, all her attention focused on the man who had followed her with such insolent assurance.

When he closed in on her she drew a deep, ragged breath and, bracing herself, waited for him to take her in his arms.

Instead he reached out and removed her glasses, ordering dispassionately, 'Get undressed.'

She could have refused, could have threatened to scream and struggle if he laid a finger on her. But, guessing that was what he was expecting, perhaps even hoping for, she refused to play into his hands.

Pale face composed, eyes blank, she took off her shoes and stockings, the light suit she'd travelled in and, after a moment's hesitation, her simple undies.

Then, proving she had both spirit and dignity, she stood proudly erect, her beautiful eyes, with their thick fringe of gold-tipped lashes, fixed on him.

Bleached to an even lighter shade by all the Italian sunshine, her hair fell like tangled silk on to her shoulders. Her skin was satin-smooth and golden, becoming camellia-pale where the sun hadn't kissed it.

'Very efficient,' he commented mockingly, and let his insolent gaze travel leisurely over her from head to toe, as though she were some slave he was thinking of buying. 'Now perhaps you'd like to do the same for me.'

'Is that an order?' she asked sweetly, and knew by the sudden tightening of his mouth that she'd managed to rattle him.

Recovering swiftly, he said, 'Merely a suggestion.'

'Then I'd rather not.' The hint of distaste was perfectly done.

Watching him strip off, and wanting to keep the initiative, she enquired recklessly, 'Would you like me to lie down?'

His teeth snapped together. 'Why be so conventional? If you're feeling accommodating, we could perhaps add a little excitement . . .'

Wishing fervently that she'd kept her mouth shut, she tried to control the shivers running through her.

Smiling a little, guessing at her panic, he stepped behind her and, cupping her breasts in his palms, drew her back against his hard body.

Thumbs stroking over her nipples, feeling them firm beneath that erotic stimulation, he put his mouth to her ear and whispered, 'Come and shower with me.'

Trying to ignore what he was doing to her, she shook her head and, her gaze fixed on the opposite wall, began to silently recite 'Daffodils', the first poem she could think of, forcing herself to concentrate on the words, distancing herself mentally.

Almost at once Adam picked up the change in her. Spinning her round, he jerked her to him with so much force that her head snapped back.

Staring down into her white face, he muttered an oath. Then, after a moment, his hands dropped to his sides. 'Forgive me,' he said tightly. 'I shouldn't have treated you in that way, but I was so bloody angry at being offloaded . . .'

Snatching up her dressing-gown, he thrust it at her and said, 'For God's sake put this on,' before turning to drag on his own clothes, his movements abrupt, jerky, lacking their usual grace and co-ordination.

'I don't understand what makes you think you were being ''off-loaded'',' she protested, pulling the gown around her and fastening the belt with unsteady hands.

His lips twisted into a smile totally without mirth. 'Because I know the routine. You see, it happened to me once before. Only I'd never dreamt that my sweet, naïve little wife would use such a trick.'

As Angie began to shake her head, he said, 'When I moved from Queensland to South Australia I had a woman with me. A woman I loved. I was even fool enough to think she loved me... Of course I was young at the time,' he added sardonically.

'Women were in short supply in Coober Pedy, and she was beautiful, so she had a choice of men. It didn't take her long to line up someone richer, more influential...'

Thrusting his shirt into his trousers, he went on tightly, 'I wouldn't have minded so much if she'd been honest and told me it was over. But, so she'd be in the clear, she tried to off-load me on to a girlfriend of hers who fancied me.'

Angie's heart ached for his disillusionment. It must have cut deep. She could see now why he'd jumped to the conclusion he had. Without meaning to, she found herself asking, 'What did you do?'

His face hard, cynical, he said, 'Her friend was... willing, to say the least, so I took advantage of the situation for as long as it suited me.'

Fully dressed now, he headed for the door.

'W-where are you going?' she faltered.

'Where do you think?'

Angie's blood seemed to turn to ice in her veins. Even though he'd described Paula as a harpy, he was going to her.

Running to him, she seized his arm. 'No, don't go. Please don't go.'

He stood quite still, looking down at her with a touch of contemptuous arrogance in his clear eyes.

Her face filled with painful colour and her hand dropped away.

The latch clicked decisively, leaving her gazing at the closed door. So Paula was going to win on both counts, take not only her home, but her husband too.

A futile anger shook her, making her tremble. She wanted to weep and curse and rail against fate.

But what good would that do? Wouldn't it be better to put up a fight?

Jerking open the door, she stumbled on to the landing just as Adam reached the bottom of the stairs.

'You're a cunning swine,' she said clearly, almost admiringly. 'But don't think I haven't guessed what your game is.'

His face full of startled surprise, he turned to look at her.

It was taking a big risk, rousing his temper even further, but heedlessly she pressed home her advantage. 'Telling me that load of twaddle just so you'd have——'

Her breath caught in her throat as he bounded back up the stairs and loomed over her. 'What "load of twaddle" is that?' he asked softly, dangerously.

Backing into the bedroom, so he was forced to follow her, she licked dry lips before saying boldly, 'You know perfectly well. All that rubbish about being off-loaded.'

She met his eyes with a confidence she was far from feeling. 'You only made it up so you could storm off and sleep with Paula.'

His dark brows lifted. 'Why should I want to sleep with Paula when I could have you?'

'Because she's beautiful and experienced and——' her voice wobbled a little '—much more exciting than I am. You wanted an excuse . . .'

A mocking smile put deep grooves beside his mouth. 'What makes you think I need an excuse?'

'Perhaps because you're as underhand and devious as the girl who ditched you in Coober Pedy.'

Some of Adam's cold rage was dying, to be replaced by a kind of reluctant amusement at Angie's stand. It was as though a small, friendly golden Labrador puppy had turned on a Doberman pinscher, and was intent on savaging it.

'You just passed an opinion that I'd invented her,' he pointed out.

'I'm sure you did. It was nothing but a colourful piece of fiction invented to justify your accusation that I was trying to pass you on to Paula.' With a catch in her voice she went on, 'When I hadn't dreamt of doing any such thing.'

His dark face showed his disbelief.

A shade desperately, she demanded, 'If I'd wanted to pass you on to Paula, would I be trying so hard to keep you here now?'

'Then why did you tell her the truth about our marriage?'

'Because of the island,' she said in a rush. 'I wanted to keep the island. But I had no legal way of proving that it had been a gift...'

Making no attempt to hide his scepticism, Adam said, 'I can understand your wanting the island, but I really don't see——'

'Not for myself,' she broke in. 'I wanted it for *you*. You'd tried to keep your side of the bargain and——'

'And you were determined to keep yours? How very noble of you.'

'Don't be so bloody offensive,' she cried furiously. 'I wanted you to have the island, the gazebo, because it meant *so much more* to you than it did to me. Because you'd shared it with your mother and loved it...' Her voice broke.

'I'm sorry,' he said quietly.

'That's what made me tell Paula about our bargain. I thought if she knew *why* I wanted the island——'

His voice brittle, he said, 'I take it she wasn't sympathetic?'

'She seemed to think it was a huge joke. I offered to buy it at its market value. I promised I would start to pay her back as soon as I'd found a job...'

Head down, Angie failed to see the raw emotion that tightened Adam's face, and went on, 'But as I couldn't give her the money immediately she wasn't interested.'

Then, feeling she was hardly being fair to Paula, she lifted her chin and explained, 'Models have a relatively short time at the top, and before her career comes to an end she's desperate to buy into the fashion business.'

Without intending to, she found herself admitting, 'In an odd sort of way I felt almost sorry for her.'

'Yes,' he said without surprise, 'meanness isn't one of your accomplishments.' After a moment he added a shade raggedly, 'I wish you'd told me all this earlier... Though I think I know why you didn't.'

He sighed deeply; then, half under his breath, as though talking to himself, muttered, 'So where do I go from here?'

Not to Paula's bed if *she* could help it, Angie vowed defiantly.

Before she could make any move, he went on, 'You said we needed to talk, and you were quite right. You've already made it clear that you want a divorce as soon as practicable...'

She didn't want a divorce at all, but obviously *he* would want one.

'But what about the short-term, the immediate problems?'

Carefully she said, 'Well, as far as I'm concerned, I need to find a job and somewhere to live. I might be able to get a bed-sit in Darfield, but there are the animals to consider.'

'I have a suggestion to make,' he said with equal care, 'bearing in mind your previous occupation... The library at Wingwood Hall is in a pretty poor state through neglect. I need a librarian to put it into order, check all the books, weed out the ones that are a total write-off, and catalogue the rest. I'll pay you the usual rate.'

Could he *afford* a librarian? she wondered. She would happily have done the work for nothing, but she had to have some kind of income to support herself.

As though reading her doubts, he said, 'If you don't take the post I'll need to engage somebody else. Of course, you may not like the idea of going through a lot of mouldering old books——'

'Oh, I *do*,' she interrupted eagerly. It was a job after her own heart. But she would have accepted a job scrubbing the Hall's floors for the sake of being close to Adam.

'Then that's settled. You can start as soon as you like. Now as for somewhere to live... The Hall would seem the logical place, so you could be on the spot, but as it's scarcely habitable I propose you stay here, at least for the time being.'

'Here?' Her heart began to throw itself against her ribs. Was he going to suggest they remain together?

Instead he said prosaically, 'It would solve the problem of the animals.'

'But what about you?' She held her breath.

'I can make shift with a sleeping-bag in the Hall. I've slept a great deal rougher.'

With a short, sharp sigh, he added, 'And, speaking of sleep, it's about time I let you get some. You've had a long, tiring day physically, not counting the emotional stress.'

'Adam...' She was almost sure, but she needed to hear him *say* it. 'You're not still angry with me, are you?'

He winced, as though the anxious question hurt him. 'No, of course I'm not still angry with you. You have far more cause to be angry with me.'

She made a negative movement with her head. Then, to wipe the slate clean, she admitted with an impish grin, 'By the way, I *don't* think you invented the woman in Coober Pedy. I only said it to make you mad and to...'

'Keep me here?' Watching her cheeks turn pink, he asked, 'Why *did* you try so hard to keep me here?'

'Because I...I didn't want you to rush off without knowing the truth.'

'Was that the only reason?'

When she didn't answer he said abruptly, 'I'd better get off to the Hall.'

'Do you have to go?' It was a mere whisper.

'I rather think I do. If I stay I might not be able to leave you alone.' His eyes brilliant, he added, 'Of course I could always take a cold shower.'

'Make it a warm one and I might join you.' Lashes lowered demurely, she added, 'I could use a spot of excitement.'

He gave a little choke of laughter, then asked severely, 'Are you quite sure you know what you're doing?'

'I think so.' Going close to him, she began to undo his shirt buttons, sliding her hand inside to lay it flat-palmed against the warmth of his chest. 'I'm trying to 'tice you.'

'You're succeeding,' he told her, looking down at her absorbed face, the softly parted lips, the sweep of gold-tipped lashes against her cheeks. 'So don't stop.'

She didn't.

And when he whispered, 'Undress me, Angel,' she needed no further urging.

Previously, despite all their intimacy, she'd been re-strained by a kind of shyness, a reluctance to make the running. Now, knowing their time together might be very brief, she threw caution to the winds and undressed him, touching and caressing the firm, bronzed flesh, and following the masculine strength of bone and whipcord muscle, as she'd always longed to.

The hiss of his breath, the way his flesh clenched as she stroked and fondled, encouraged her.

A sense of her own power sent her soaring, like a runaway balloon, to dizzy heights as she realised how easily she could disturb him, make him feel the same kind of heated excitement and pleasure that he aroused in her.

Then common sense pricked the balloon and brought her down to earth with a thud, stilling her hands. He was a virile, red-blooded man; presumably almost any woman would be able to elicit the same response.

Still, she told herself sturdily, *she* was the here-and-now woman, and she was also, for the moment at least, his wife.

Her hands began to move again, and Adam carefully released the breath he'd been holding.

For a while he let her play, enjoying her innocent enjoyment, reacting to the stimulus of her untutored hands, her artless eroticism, which turned him on to a fever pitch no experienced woman had ever managed to achieve.

Only then did he start to return the kisses and caresses, giving her back the delight she had given him, driving her wild with longing before sweeping her into his arms and muttering, 'To hell with the shower. Let's make it the bed.'

Her face buried against the warm column of his throat, she complained, 'I think you're mean. You promised me some excitement.'

Highly amused, he retorted, 'You'll get as much excitement as you can stand for one night. Tomorrow we'll try the shower.'

Tomorrow we'll try the shower.

His words were like a precious gift, holding so much more than the obvious meaning: a declaration that tomorrow they would still be together; a hope, at least, for the immediate future.

CHAPTER TEN

ADAM said nothing further about sleeping at the Hall, and, though Angie felt as if she were walking a tightrope slung across Niagara, she determined to let things ride.

He was with her, and she was satisfied just to live from day to day. Any talk of the future might only disturb the status quo and precipitate the move she feared.

On Monday evening they were sitting over the remains of a leisurely meal when, a frown drawing her fine silky brows together, Angie asked, 'What have you done to your hands?'

Glancing down at his skinned knuckles, he answered, 'Just scraped them a bit when I took the car into town this afternoon to fill up with oil and petrol.'

Adam's reply, though cheerfully casual, held an odd satisfaction which made a sudden suspicion leap into her mind, a suspicion fuelled by the realisation that he'd kept his hands out of sight as much as possible.

His expression was so determinedly bland, however, that after a moment's consideration Angie abandoned her intention to probe further, and said instead, 'They look sore. I'll get something to put on them.'

As she moved past him he caught her wrist and pulled her on to his knee. 'I've a better idea. Kiss me and take my mind off them . . .'

Over the next couple of weeks they established an easy, pleasant routine. Except for their sex life. That was dynamic and exciting and as far from routine as paradise was from the mundane world.

All her happiness, fragile as eggshell china, lay in the palm of his hand, but, while he never mentioned love or affection, his desire for her seemed unabated, and, thinking how it might have been, she could only be grateful.

After breakfasting together, Adam would drive Angie over to the Hall to wage war on the library while he dealt with estate business.

If the weather was good they shared a picnic lunch outdoors. When it wasn't they made shift in a large stone-flagged kitchen, which appeared to have been altered little since Victorian times.

Each day, in an effort to combat the damp, he stoked the huge furnace which heated the old-fashioned radiators, and, when it was fine, opened the mullioned windows wide to air the place.

To Angie's great but unspoken relief they saw nothing of Paula. Mrs Pimm, who popped round frequently to tidy up, restock the larder, and let Tosca in and out, reported, 'She goes off after breakfast every day in that car of hers, and doesn't come back until it's dark.'

On Friday morning Angie was making toast in the kitchen at Fife Cottage when Adam strolled in, wearing an immaculate white shirt and a well-cut grey suit.

Her heart leapt at the sight of him. Dressed with some degree of formality, he looked even more dangerously attractive.

Touching his lips to the warmth of her nape, making her shiver deliciously, he told her, 'I won't be needing any lunch, Angel. I've an appointment at the bank and a full day's business to get through.'

Biting back an absurd feeling of disappointment—their alfresco lunches were precious to her—she asked, 'Will you want dinner at the usual time?'

He frowned briefly. 'I may have to eat out; it all depends. If I'm not home by seven, presume I won't be coming.'

Despite his determinedly light tone, there was a tension about him that made her uneasy. Was he worried over money? Concerned about his meeting with the bank?

Breakfast over, he said briskly, 'If you're going to the Hall today I'll drop you on the way into town. Unless you want to take your own car so you'll have transport home?'

'It looks like being a nice day, so I'll walk back.' She would be in no hurry to get home if Adam wasn't going to be there.

He drove the short distance to the Hall in silence, his expression abstracted, faintly austere, his mouth a concentrated line.

They had reached their destination and drawn to a halt before he roused himself to remark, 'The plumbers will be making a start next Monday...'

Knowing an efficient central-heating system for a place the size of Wingwood Hall—not to mention modernising the kitchen and several bathrooms—wouldn't come cheap, she wondered how he'd manage to pay them. But perhaps he was trying to negotiate a loan from the bank.

'And they should be followed by the builders.'

'Is there a lot of work for them?'

'The original survey I had done suggests that structurally there isn't a great deal wrong. Once the roof's been fixed and a few windows replaced we can start thinking about redecorating and restoring some of the furniture and fittings.'

Well, that didn't sound like a man who was too worried financially, Angie thought with relief.

And he'd said 'we', for a moment warming and loosening the cold, tight, steely band of fear for the future that encircled her heart, a fear she fought hard to ignore in case it spoilt the present.

As she got out of the car he grimaced at his white cuffs and said quizzically, 'I'm hardly dressed for stoking, so I'll give you a wonderful opportunity to demonstrate the equality of women...'

'You're all heart!'

He grinned briefly. 'Aren't I just?'

She was standing in the sunshine, smiling, waiting...

'Have fun.' When he spun the wheel and drove away without kissing her goodbye she felt suddenly, indescribably depressed, deserted as any Ariadne.

Standing looking after the white hatchback, she felt the prick of foolish tears and had to blink hard.

Who said love brought only joy and happiness? she thought vexedly. It brought melancholy and heartache, turned a healthy, robust young woman into a weak, wilting shadow...

Pulling herself up short, she caught her fleeing sense of humour by the scruff of its neck and gave it a good shake. This weak, wilting shadow had a large furnace to stoke. Hard work would almost certainly prove to be the panacea for all that ailed her.

And it did. By nine-thirty she had sweated off what felt like a stone in weight and regained her normal cheerful aspect.

Having taken a spluttering, scalding shower in the closest of the antiquated bathrooms and dried herself on an old towel she'd dug out of the airing cupboard, Angie made herself a coffee and carried it through to the library.

The familiar musty smell of decaying leather, printer's ink and mildewing paper greeted her.

Fiercely protective of books, before getting down to work she allowed herself a black thought or two about the man who had left old and rare volumes—irreplaceable first editions—to moulder away.

Lunchtime lacked its normal sparkle, but as soon as she got involved in her work again the afternoon seemed to fly.

Deciding to stay until six-thirty, she had just wheeled a beautiful old pulpit-staircase into position to enable her to examine some heavy, morocco-bound books on the top shelf, when the sound of footsteps startled her.

Peering down from her elevated perch, hoping, with a sudden surge of gladness, to see Adam, she was staggered to find that her unexpected visitor was Simon.

'Hello,' she called without enthusiasm.

He looked up, tilting back his sleek blond head. 'So there you are.'

Wondering what had brought Simon to Wingwood Hall, she asked, 'How did you know where to find me?'

'When I couldn't raise you at Fife Cottage I called at Clouds, and Paula's housekeeper told me you'd probably still be here.'

All in all he seemed very *au fait* with the situation, Angie decided a shade crossly, and, wishing that Mrs Pimm had kept mum about her whereabouts, she descended the narrow wooden steps.

Looking as if he'd like to hold his nose, Simon muttered, 'How you can work in an atmosphere like this beats me.'

'I don't notice it after a while,' she assured him cheerfully.

'Look, would you mind if we talked outside?'

She was about to ask what they had to talk about when she noticed the tell-tale marks along his jawline and beneath his left eye. They were fading now, but there was no doubt that the bruises had been colourful.

It was too much of a coincidence when she recalled Adam's skinned knuckles, his voice saying with deceptive mildness, 'I must have a few words with that gentleman'.

'What happened?' she demanded. 'Did Adam...?'

Simon glowered. 'He damn near broke my jaw... But, let me tell you, he didn't have it all his own way. I knocked him down before he'd laid so much as a finger on me.'

'Really?' Though Simon was almost as tall as Adam, he wasn't nearly as powerful, and, remembering how he'd run like a rabbit when Adam had tacitly threatened him, Angie found it hard to believe that he'd taken the offensive.

Reacting to her expression, Simon snapped, 'You don't have to take *my* word for it; someone else was there and saw me floor him.'

'I'm impressed,' she said admiringly. 'Or did you take him by surprise?'

Judging by the dark colour that seeped along Simon's cheekbones, she'd hit the nail right on the head.

Ignoring her sally, he persisted peevishly, 'I hate this damned smell. Can't we get out of here?'

'What did you come for?' she asked, following him across the hall, its stone-flagged floor patterned with elongated lozenges of light, and through the open door into the sunshine.

'I've come to warn you.'

It sounded so melodramatic that she almost laughed. 'Warn me?'

'About what that "husband" of yours is getting up to...'

When she made no move to take the bait, Simon went on, 'I don't suppose you're aware he's seeing Paula.'

'What makes you think that?'

'I don't *think*, I *know*. She was with him the day he came to my office looking for trouble. He'd asked her to wait in the car, I gather, and wasn't any too pleased when she followed him in.'

'Is that all?' Angie queried with icy disdain.

'Not by a long chalk. I've seen him with her several times, and I happen to know they're having dinner together this evening.'

Gathering herself, determined not to let him see how badly he'd shaken her, she asked curtly, 'How do you know?'

'Paula told me. She's leaving for London tonight, and she doesn't expect to be alone. So don't be surprised if he doesn't come home.'

Feeling a kind of sick despair, Angie realised it fitted. It all fitted. He'd gone out dressed for the metropolis, and he could easily have put his case in the boot of the car without her knowing...

No, she couldn't—*wouldn't*—believe it. He might not love her, but after all the joy and laughter and passion they'd shared he wouldn't treat her like that, wouldn't go without a word.

Slowly she shook her head. 'I don't believe *any* of it.'

'You'd better believe it. It happens to be the truth.'

Scornfully she came up with a retort from her school-days. 'You wouldn't know the truth if it came up and bit your bum.'

For a moment he was shocked into silence, then, re-covering his assurance, he told her triumphantly, 'I can prove it.'

'Very well.' She threw down the gauntlet. 'Prove it.'

Disconcerted now, he hesitated, his mouth sulky. 'Well, if you refuse to take my word for it you'll have to come into Darfield with me.'

'Give me a minute to wash my hands and lock up.'

Pale blue eyes took in her bare legs and sandalled feet, her oatmeal cotton skirt and button-through top. 'Are you coming dressed like that?' His disapproval was evident.

'What you see is what you get,' she said jauntily.

'Well, at least do something with your hair.' The old Simon was back.

Face and hands washed, her pale knot of hair tidied into a fairly respectable chignon, she took her place beside him in the Mercedes and tried not to feel anxious as they drove into town.

She *believed* in Adam, in his basic kindness and integrity. He might be tempted by Paula's blatant sexuality, but he wouldn't go about things in such an underhand way, she thought a shade confusedly.

Yet Simon seemed so sure of his facts.

When they turned into the old part of town, before they'd even reached the cul-de-sac Angie guessed where they were heading. Men tended to be creatures of habit and, in some things, Adam was no exception.

Though it was still quite early, Carriages appeared to be busy, and as usual quite a few posh cars were drawn up on the fine gravel apron in front of the restaurant.

Among them was Adam's white hatchback, and further along the street she'd glimpsed a red sports car that could have been Paula's.

'Seen enough?'

Simon's gloating tone roused all Angie's fighting spirit. 'Not by a long chalk,' she said positively. 'And now we've come all this way I expect you'd like to have dinner here.'

His expression made it clear that nothing had been further from his thoughts. 'I'm not really——'

'Well, I certainly would.' She was already climbing out of the car.

With relief he admitted, 'I don't think we stand much chance of getting a table.'

She raised a derisory brow.

'It isn't just a matter of money,' he added, his pride clearly suffering. 'The owner's a snobbish so-and-so and——'

'If it should prove necessary, perhaps you could mention that I'm Lady Wingwood.'

'But you're not dressed for eating out,' he objected, sounding both resentful and panicky.

'A title covers a multitude of sins, in case you hadn't noticed.'

Taking a last-ditch stand, Simon muttered, 'But suppose *he* sees us?'

'Scared?' she taunted.

'Certainly not,' he said, earning her admiration. Then, looking like Daniel about to enter the lions' den, he locked the Mercedes and followed her to the door of the restaurant.

Uncertain what she was trying to prove, Angie began to repent her rash stubbornness the moment she was through the door. If Adam *was* here—and surely he *must* be, or what was his car doing outside?—she was only laying herself wide open to misery and scorn.

Unless he was alone.

He wasn't.

She spotted them almost straight away, sitting at a table for two by the far window, Adam as she'd last seen him dressed, Paula wearing a stunning outfit in black and white zigzags.

They appeared to be totally wrapped up in each other.

Wanting to turn tail and run, Angie found herself being escorted with some ceremony—proving that a title was more important than dress—to an alcove table opposite.

Trapped, she was forced to sit through the most wretched meal she had ever endured, while Simon, on edge and jumpy, stayed silent, clearly wishing himself anywhere but where he was.

Leaving it up to him to order, she ate whatever the waiter put before her without tasting a thing, all her attention fixed on the far table.

The two were in profile, lingering over their coffee and talking intimately, dark heads inclined towards each other.

Their tête-à-tête was interrupted briefly while Adam paid the bill. Then Paula put out a slim, scarlet-tipped hand and, when Adam took it and held it, she leaned forward and kissed him on the mouth. A moment later they got up to go.

They made a striking pair and, unable to look away, Angie watched covertly until the door had closed behind them.

Feeling as though she'd been stabbed through the heart, she was staring blindly at the green cloth when a voice enquired coolly, 'Enjoyed your meal?'

Doubting her own ears, she looked up into Adam's dark face.

'I thought you'd gone,' she said stupidly.

His smile was thin-lipped. 'I merely saw Paula to her car.'

Leaning towards Simon, who was sitting as though he were stuffed, Adam said softly, almost pleasantly, 'If I ever catch you within a mile of my wife again I'll break your neck. Is that clear?'

'B-but I haven't...I didn't...'

Ignoring the stammered words, Adam asked, 'Ready, Angel?' His hand beneath her elbow brooked no argument, and, stunned, Angie allowed herself to be half lifted to her feet and led out of the restaurant and across to the car.

'Get in,' he ordered tersely.

She was about to protest at his high-handedness when a quelling glance made her change her mind.

Having settled her in the front passenger seat, he got behind the wheel and drove back to Fife Cottage without a word.

His expression was grim, unrelenting, almost as if *she* was the one who had transgressed, Angie thought, with a mixture of anger and uncertainty.

But beneath the confusion there was the dawning of a tenuous joy. Even if his face was like thunder, he was here with her, not on his way to London with Paula.

Mrs Pimm had left Tosca in the garden, and they were forced to run the gauntlet of the bull-terrier's rapturous welcome before they could escape into the house.

In the living-room they faced each other.

The question bristling with accusation, Adam demanded, 'What the hell were you doing with Perry?'

'Watching you with Paula,' she retorted, golden eyes flashing, 'holding her hand and kissing her.'

'I didn't kiss Paula. *She* kissed me. And we were *shaking* hands, which is somewhat different.'

Angie let that go and attacked from another angle. 'You've been meeting her regularly behind my back.'

His eyes glinted green. 'You sound just like a jealous wife.'

'Well, haven't you?'

'Yes,' he admitted coolly.

Her heart dropped liked a stone. Even after seeing them together she'd been hoping Simon had been lying, hoping tonight was a one-off, something that could be explained away.

'And how many times have you met Perry behind *my* back?'

'You sound just like a jealous husband,' she mocked, wanting to hurt him the way he was hurting her.

He took her upper arms, his fingers biting in, and jerked her towards him. Looking down into her startled face, he snarled, 'That's exactly what I am! How many?'

She defied him. 'How many times have you slept with Paula?' Instantly she regretted changing 'met' into 'slept with', but it was too late.

Her inference made sheer blazing anger emanate from him. Controlling it, he said silkily, 'None, would you believe? But as *you* seem to be in need of an extramarital relationship, it's obvious I've been neglecting you... And we can't have that, can we?'

Deliberately he put a hand over the curve of her breast, his teasing thumb unerringly finding its goal.

'Leave me alone!' Scared of the devil she'd released, she tried to pull free.

His mouth curved into a cruel little smile. 'Oh, no, my Angel. That's the last thing I intend to do...'

But, his hand dropping away, he moved back.

She was breathing a sigh of relief when, with a couple of quick jerks, he pulled the rose-patterned curtains over the window, shutting out the bright evening.

'I'm going to make love to you until you're sated... And *I'll* decide when that is.'

Sloughing his jacket, he unknotted his blue and white tie and pulled it free of his collar. Then slowly, purposefully, he began to undo his shirt buttons.

Refusing to run, she stood her ground and watched while he pulled the shirt free of his trousers and tossed it over a chair.

Her certainty that he was bluffing took a tumble when he reached for, and unfastened, the clip and zip of his trousers and slid them down over lean hips.

She swallowed convulsively, her throat desert-dry.

Reaching out, he removed her glasses, and said softly, dangerously, 'It always excites me to do that. You look at me with those big eyes, half seductive, half vulnerable. It's like taking off a yashmak, having my own private woman... Except that you're not my own. I seem to be sharing you with Perry...'

Slipping his fingers under the neckline of the fine lawn top she was wearing, with a quick wrench he tore it apart, ripping the buttons from the buttonholes. Then, paying no heed to her gasp of outrage, he unclipped her bra and tossed it aside.

Before she could lasso her scattered wits, her feet were hooked from under her, and she found herself flat on her back on the floor.

He followed her down, and with deftness and speed removed the rest of her clothing.

Aware that it would be useless, she made no attempt to struggle, but lay still and quiet, holding on to her anger, using it as a shield.

A shaft of low evening sun slanted beneath the curtains and fell across her face, turning her eyes to molten gold and the wisps of hair escaping from her chignon to strands of bright silk.

He cupped her cheek with his palm, brushing the pad of his thumb over her lips. 'You've a mouth that could drive any man wild... An enticing body... No wonder Perry wants you...'

In a low, husky voice he went on, 'But I want you *more*, and not just your body. I want your sweet, secret self, your mind, your thoughts, open to me. I want to be able to control your emotions, to make you *feel*, to be the only man in your life.'

His hands moved over her, stroking, caressing, bringing a singing excitement.

If he'd tried to take her roughly, her mind at least could have held out against him, but this blissful, beguiling seduction made her entire being melt.

When her body was soft and yielding, his hard and purposeful, yet curiously gentle, he spanned her slim waist with his hands and fitted himself into the waiting cradle of her hips.

With a fierce delight she felt his mouth at her breast, felt him moving deep inside her, each strong thrust building up a spiralling core of sensation that climaxed in an explosion of mindless ecstasy.

Love for him overwhelmed her as, breath rasping, chest heaving, he buried his face in the warm hollow of her throat.

After lying quiescent for a while they made love again. And yet again. Each time she was ready, eager for him.

As the sexual excitement loosened its grip and the euphoria gradually faded, Angie became aware of the discomfort of her position. She was taking most of Adam's weight, the floor was hard, and there was a cool draught coming under the front door.

She shook him. 'I'm getting cold...'

Lifting his dark head, which had been cradled on her breast, he muttered something she didn't catch, and, getting to his feet, reached down a strong hand and hauled her up. 'Come on, you'd better have a hot shower and get ready for bed. I'll let the dog in and then we need to talk. I want to know why you were with Perry.'

Easing the stiff muscles of her back, she rejoined with spirit, 'And I want to know why you were with Paula.'

Some twenty minutes later, freshly showered, and demure in her daisy-patterned nightdress, she sat propped up with pillows in a pool of light shed by the bedside lamp, in her hand the mug of hot milk liberally laced with brandy that Adam had brought her.

Though she looked serene, inwardly she was churning. This was the show-down, the coming to grips with reality and the future that she'd been trying to avoid while delicately walking her tightrope.

As she put the empty mug down, the latch clicked and Adam appeared, totally naked, his dark hair still damp from the shower, and got into bed beside her.

Without preamble, he said, 'Let's have it.'

After a glance at his uncompromising expression, she obeyed.

'Just after six this evening, when I was still at the Hall, Simon turned up. He told me you were seeing Paula, that you were having dinner together.' Her voice wavered a little. 'He said——'

'Perry's said a damned sight too much if you ask me. I thought he'd learned his lesson last time when——'

'When you beat him up?'

'When I warned him to keep his nose out of our business. Unfortunately Paula followed me in, and having an audience made him behave foolishly.'

'He said you nearly broke his jaw.'

'An overstatement, I'm sure. But I obviously hurt his pride enough to make him want to get his own back. What else did he tell you?'

'That Paula was going to London tonight and didn't expect to be alone... I didn't want to believe it, but you'd gone out dressed for town, and I——'

'Why didn't you want to believe it?'

'W-what?' she stammered.

'*Why* didn't you want to believe it?' he repeated inexorably.

'Because I... I...'

'Love me?'

Unable to admit her love until *he'd* given some sign he cared, she stayed mute.

His face growing bleak, Adam asked, 'Do you still love Simon?'

'No, I don't still love Simon. I'm not sure I ever did.'

She heard his expelled breath, before she asked, 'Do you love Paula?'

'You must be joking!'

'Do you *want* her, then?'

'No.' His denial was bald and uncompromising. 'That kind of predatory woman has never appealed to me.'

'Then why have you been seeing her?'

'We've been going to Mason's.'

'Mason's?' She was startled. 'You mean Ben's solicitor?'

'That's right. I've been negotiating to buy...'

'Of course,' Angie breathed as he paused, *the island.*'

'The price I offered her was well over the odds, and with the solicitor's agreement she was getting it straight away instead of in a year's time, so I was fairly sure she'd sell. But she enjoyed keeping me on a string, pretending to blow hot and cold.

'We finally smoothed out the last of the legal tangles and signed the documents late this afternoon.

'Afterwards she wanted me to take her out for a meal, and, feeling I owed her that much, I agreed.'

'But why did she tell Simon you'd be going to London with her?'

'Before signing the contract, she made it clear that she expected *me* to be part of the deal.' His beautiful mouth ruthless, he went on, 'I didn't correct that assumption. At least not until we left Carriages and I escorted her out to her car.' His eyes were cold, full of contempt.

Angie felt almost sorry for Paula.

After a moment she said slowly, 'I'm so *glad* you've got the island back, but I wanted you to have it without borrowing from the bank.'

'I haven't borrowed from the bank.'

'Oh, but I thought... I mean, I know you haven't any money, and you did mention a meeting with the bank.'

He sighed. 'Because of the chaos and the debts my father left, everyone believes I'm a pauper.'

'And you're not?'

'Most definitely not.' He smiled at her surprise.

'Why didn't you tell me before?'

'For the same reason I delayed telling you I was Adam Wingwood. Judging what kind of woman you were, what your reaction would be, I wanted you to get to know me first. I thought if I told you the truth too soon it might frighten you off.'

Delighted to hear he wasn't in financial straits, she began, 'But if your father left nothing but debts, how did you . . . ? I mean, where did you . . . ?'

'Six years ago I bought an old, abandoned mine in Coober Pedy. It was thought to be worked out, so I got it for a song.

'Eighteen back-breaking months later I was about to throw in my hand and start working for someone else when I struck a magnificent vein of first-class opal. Overnight, almost, I became a wealthy man.'

He put a finger beneath her chin. 'Your mouth's open.'

In a strangled voice she asked, 'But if you had plenty of money to buy the island, why did you agree to marry me?'

'I *could* say it was because you'd refused to sell, but, if you recall, I mentioned another reason, which I promised to tell you at the end of our year together. Only then,' he added cryptically, 'I discovered I hadn't got a year.'

Crossly she said, 'You once told me that as a child you liked conundrums, but I wish you wouldn't talk in riddles.'

He grinned and kissed her ear. 'Very well. A couple of days before our wedding, the London detective I'd hired reported that Paula had been married in a Chelsea register office.'

'You knew *before* the wedding! But why did you go through with it?'

'Because I *wanted* to marry you. I had some stupid idea that if we were really man and wife I could make you forget Perry and love me.'

A giant fist seemed to squeeze her heart. 'Why did you want me to love you?' The world stopped turning and came to a standstill while she waited for his answer.

'You heard me tell both Perry and Paula that on my part it had been love at first sight.'

'I didn't think you meant it,' she said faintly.

'Oh, yes, I meant it.' A shade wryly he added, 'It was instant enchantment. I thought about you, dreamt about you, fantasised over you like some callow schoolboy. You had everything I'd ever wanted in a woman: sense, sweetness, spirit, and, beneath that cool, rather prim exterior, a depth of warmth and passion I'd never hoped to find.'

The most wonderful feeling of joy and happiness she'd ever known spread through her. 'But on our honeymoon, when I asked if you loved me, you said no.'

'It was too early to let you know how I felt. At that stage I believed you still loved Simon, and I didn't want to alarm you by seeming to ask for an emotional commitment you were unable to give, or burdening you with one you didn't want.'

'You knew I wanted you,' she objected.

'You might have *wanted* me, but that isn't the same as loving. The only reason you'd married me was to keep Clouds. I was haunted by the thought that when we returned home and you found Paula had got to the altar first, so to speak, you might go back to Simon. That's why I seduced you. I knew I had only a short time to try and oust him from your mind, try to make you reliant on me, even if it was only for your physical pleasure. I was completely thrown to find you were still a virgin. I bitterly regretted what I'd done, how I'd messed up your life.

'Then after that day in Bellazzo things seemed to be working out. You appeared to be enjoying our honeymoon and I began to have high hopes for the future. I'd half expected that when we got back Paula would have taken up residence next door. What I hadn't expected was your reaction. You were so *shattered* I felt an absolute swine. Although you'd been desperate enough to propose to a virtual stranger to keep Clouds, it wasn't until then that I realised *fully* how much the place meant to you.'

His fingers gently massaged her nape. 'I was hoping to actually have the deeds before I told you, but——'

'You mean you bought not just the island but everything? *You* own Clouds?'

'No, *you* do. The only way I could make amends was to give you the cottage as a gift...'

Oh, Ben, she breathed silently, I hope you're listening.

'You can move back in there as soon as you like.'

Somehow she made her voice casual. 'Before I do that, I rather fancy a second honeymoon.'

She felt Adam's absolute stillness. 'Where would you like to go?'

'What about the Villa dei Fiori? Do you think they'll lend it to you again?'

'I own it. It was one of the first things I bought when I struck it rich.'

'In that case, if you can spare the time...'

Softly he assured her, 'I can spare the time.'

'Then I'll move into Clouds when we get back.' Watching his face, she added primly, 'I know you don't like forward women, but will you be moving in with me?'

'I thought you'd never ask, you teasing witch.'

For a while he just held her tightly, his cheek against her hair, then he queried, 'And when the Hall's done, what then?'

'Perhaps I could move in with you. We could let Mrs Pimm look after Clouds.'

'Won't it be a wrench to leave your home?'

'Yes,' she said honestly. 'But now home is where you are, and I'm sure Ben will understand.'

Snuggling closer, she confided, 'I fell in love at first sight with Wingwood Hall, the same as I did with its master... And just think of all those lovely bedrooms.'

When he drew back a little and raised a dark brow, she explained, 'For our children.'

'How many were you planning on having?'

'Six is a nice round number,' she suggested.

Looking thoughtful, he said, 'If we're aiming for six, perhaps we'd better make a start.'

'Can you manage it again?' she asked saucily.

He laughed. 'Try me, my Angel.'

She did.

And he did.

4 FREE

Romances and 2 FREE gifts just for you!

*You can enjoy all the
heartwarming emotion of true love for FREE!
Discover the heartbreak and happiness,
the emotion and the tenderness of the modern
relationships in Mills & Boon Romances.*

*We'll send you 4 Romances as a special offer
from Mills & Boon Reader Service,
along with the opportunity to have 6 captivating
new Romances delivered to your door each month.*

Claim your FREE books and gifts overleaf...

An irresistible offer
from Mills & Boon

Become a regular reader of Romances with Mills & Boon Reader Service and we'll welcome you with 4 books, a CUDDLY TEDDY and a special MYSTERY GIFT all absolutely FREE.

And then look forward to receiving 6 brand new Romances each month, delivered to your door hot off the presses, postage and packing FREE! Plus our free Newsletter featuring author news, competitions, special offers and much more.

This invitation comes with no strings attached. You may cancel or suspend your subscription at any time, and still keep your free books and gifts.

It's so easy. Send no money now. Simply fill in the coupon below and post it to -
Reader Service, FREEPOST, PO Box 236, Croydon, Surrey CR9 9EL.

— — — — NO STAMP REQUIRED — — — —

Free Books Coupon

Yes! Please rush me 4 FREE Romances and 2 FREE gifts! Please also reserve me a Reader Service subscription. If I decide to subscribe I can look forward to receiving 6 brand new Romances for just £11.40 each month, postage and packing FREE. If I decide not to subscribe I shall write to you within 10 days - I can keep the free books and gifts whatever I choose. I may cancel or suspend my subscription at any time. I am over 18 years of age.

Ms/Mrs/Miss/Mr _____ EP71R

Address _____

_____

Postcode _____ Signature _____

Offers closes 31st October 1994. The right is reserved to refuse an application and change the terms of this offer. One application per household. Offer not available for current subscribers to Mills & Boon Romances. Offer only valid in UK and Eire. Overseas readers please write for details. Southern Africa write to IBS Private Bag X3010, Randburg 2125. You may be mailed with offers from other reputable companies as a result of this application. Please tick box if you would prefer not to receive such offers. ☐

mps
MAILING
PREFERENCE
SERVICE

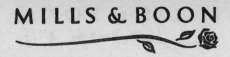

MILLS & BOON

HEARTS OF FIRE by Miranda Lee

Welcome to our compelling family saga set in the glamorous world of opal dealing in Australia. Laden with dark secrets, forbidden desires and scandalous discoveries, **Hearts of Fire** unfolds over a series of 6 books, but each book also features a passionate romance with a happy ending and can be read independently.

Book 1: SEDUCTION & SACRIFICE
Published: April 1994   *FREE* with Book 2

Lenore had loved Zachary Marsden secretly for years. Loyal, handsome and protective, Zachary was the perfect husband. Only Zachary would never leave his wife…would he?

WATCH OUT for special promotions!

Book 2: DESIRE & DECEPTION
Published: April 1994   Price £2.50

Jade had a name for Kyle Armstrong: *Mr Cool*. He was the new marketing manager at Whitmore Opals—the job *she* coveted. However, the more she tried to hate this usurper, the more she found him attractive…

Book 3: PASSION & THE PAST
Published: May 1994   Price £2.50

Melanie was intensely attracted to Royce Grantham—which shocked her! She'd been so sure after the tragic end of her marriage that she would never feel for any man again. How strong was her resolve not to repeat past mistakes?

MILLS & BOON

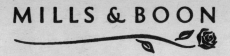

HEARTS OF FIRE by Miranda Lee

Book 4: FANTASIES & THE FUTURE
Published: June 1994   Price £2.50

The man who came to mow the lawns was more stunning than any of Ava's fantasies, though she realised that Vincent Morelli thought she was just another rich, lonely housewife looking for excitement! But, Ava knew that her narrow, boring existence was gone forever...

Book 5: SCANDALS & SECRETS
Published: July 1994   Price £2.50

Celeste Campbell had lived on her hatred of Byron Whitmore for twenty years. Revenge was sweet...until news reached her that Byron was considering remarriage. Suddenly she found she could no longer deny all those long-buried feelings for him...

Book 6: MARRIAGE & MIRACLES
Published: August 1994   Price £2.50

Gemma's relationship with Nathan was in tatters, but her love for him remained intact—she was going to win him back! Gemma knew that Nathan's terrible past had turned his heart to stone, and she was asking for a miracle. But it was possible that one could happen, wasn't it?

Don't miss all six books!

HEARTS OF FIRE

By Miranda Lee

HEARTS OF FIRE by Miranda Lee is a totally compelling six-part saga set in Australia's glamorous but cut-throat world of gem dealing.

Discover the passion, scandal, sin and finally the hope that exists between two fabulously rich families. You'll be hooked from the very first page…

Each of the six novels in this series features a gripping romance. And the first title **SEDUCTION AND SACRIFICE** can be yours absolutely FREE! You can also reserve the remaining five novels in this exciting series from Reader Service, delivered to your door for £2.50 each. And remember postage and packing is FREE!

MILLS & BOON READER SERVICE, FREEPOST, P.O. BOX 236, CROYDON CR9 9EL. TEL: 061-684 2141

- -

YES! Please send me my FREE book (part 1 in the Hearts of Fire series) and reserve me a subscription for the remaining 5 books in the series. I understand that you will send me one book each month and invoice me £2.50 each month.

NO STAMP NEEDED

MILLS & BOON READER SERVICE, FREEPOST, P.O. BOX 236, CROYDON CR9 9EL. TEL: 061-684 2141

Ms/Mrs/Miss/Mr: EPHOF
_____

Address
_____

_____

                                                      Postcode
_____